TOURING BIKES

TOURING BIKES

A PRACTICAL GUIDE

Tony Oliver

The Crowood Press

First published in 1990 by
The Crowood Press Ltd
Ramsbury, Marlborough
Wiltshire SN8 2HR

This impression 1992

British Library Cataloguing in Publication Data

Oliver, Tony
  Touring bikes.
  1. Bicycles
  I. Title
  629.2272

  ISBN 1 85223 339 7

Dedication
To the memory of my parents who encouraged my love of cycling
and the outdoors.

Set in 11/12 pt Palatino

Typeset by Acorn Bookwork, Salisbury, Wiltshire
Printed in Great Britain at The Bath Press

Contents

Acknowledgements

I am especially grateful to the many people who have assisted with technical information, particularly about Reynolds, Columbus, Vitus and Tange tubing; to Dick for reading the text through and so delightfully pointing out the obvious; to Jacqui and Emyr for slaving over many of the drawings – the better ones I hasten to add; to Pete who encouraged me to write in the cycling press in the first place; and a special thanks to Chris, who had to put up with my moods when the words wouldn't come proper.

Except where credited, all photographs were taken and printed by the author. A Canon F1 with a 100mm macro lens was used for the great majority of the shots, loaded with Ilford FP4, HP5 or PanF as appropriate. Thanks to those who allowed their bikes to be used as models. Next time perhaps you could clean them first?

To a non-cyclist the apparently random use of inches and millimetres throughout this book may seem confusing – it is confusing – even to me within the cycle trade. I have tried to follow the accepted norm as it is these that flow naturally off cyclists' tongues. For example, most bicycle tubes throughout the world, except in France, have imperial diameters (inches). Crank lengths, however, are universally measured in millimetres. The width of older English tyres are described in inches; the width of modern 700c tyres are measured in millimetres.

Foreword

Many years ago, in a previous incarnation as a physicist, we needed an experimentalist in the place where I was working and advertised the job. One candidate, the best by far as it turned out, turned up on a bike, in full cycling kit including shorts. He asked if there was somewhere that he could use in order to change into his interview kit – if we really thought it necessary. We didn't. We offered him the job, but he said he would like to come back to talk to us about it before accepting. He wanted to interview us, to make sure that there would be time for his proposed solo bike trip around Iceland and to make sure that we wouldn't get on one another's nerves. He liked us, accepted the job and Tony Oliver and I have been friends ever since.

When we go off together we travel on foot, by kayak or, lately, by dog-sledge as I am not a dedicated cyclist. He did persuade me on to a mountain bike, although he had to get me all the way to Svalbard to do it. Frequently on these trips our talks would be about bikes, their design and construction. I was around when he started building frames and was always fascinated by the common sense he brought to the job and the way he was completely unmoved by the hype offered by manufacturers and 'experts'. Tony's knowledge came from his understanding of physics, engineering and metallurgy, but also – and far more importantly it seemed to me – from his knowledge of cycling. Too many people seem to ignore the cyclist in their search for innovation – usually more imagined than real – and a quick profit.

For several years I have been trying to persuade Tony to put his thoughts down for the benefit of the cycling community. I am delighted that he has finally done so.

Richard Sale
1989

7

Introduction

I still cannot climb to Pen-y-Pass without memories of my first crossing flooding back. It might have been only a BSA with a three-speed Sturmey Archer and a borrowed fiver from my dad to keep me quiet during the school holidays, but it was magic. In the years since, I have graduated from BSA to hand-built dream machine, but the excitement remains the same.

For many years I strongly believed that frames, indeed bikes, were much less important than cyclists and to an extent I still believe that to be true. I have learned, though, that cyclists will benefit from a good frame, one that allows them to use their energy most efficiently. In this book I have tried to explain why this is so.

All aspects of frame design and construction are considered – metals, tube choice, angles and sizes. Small frames, large frames and frames for ladies who still want to ride with a dropped top tube are all included, as is the newest arrival on the scene, the all-terrain bike (ATB). To complete the picture I have also considered bicycles other than the standard single, such as tandems, trikes and triplets. This is nothing unusual for a frame builder; we often get roped into one-offs such as triplets with doggy side-cars, racing pedal-cars and human-powered vehicles. That might sound like an indulgence, but it is not. I learned a lot from having to consider the needs of these machines and I believe this is of benefit to the simple cycle.

The sections on frame design are fol-lowed by one on components. Cycle-component making is big business and the cyclist is often asked to pay a lot of hard-earned cash for these parts. But does he always get value for money and, more importantly, are all these new designs, metals and gismos really necessary and will they prove reliable? If you are pedal-ling 20,000 miles every year, some of it in remote places, it is important that each component continues to function, not that it is the latest fad. I hope I will be able to shed some light on these matters. Finally there is a section aimed at touring, which considers gear carrying and a few other specifics. Perhaps you will be able to benefit from some of my experiences; I certainly hope so.

Perhaps now that I have told you what is in the book I should be honest about what is not. This book is not about how to build a frame or a wheel or how to put the whole lot together. It is about the philosophy of bike building, about the things that need considering before you upgrade and how simply to maximise your enjoyment. It should start you thinking about what it is you want, so that when you go to your supplier you will be less inclined to suffer what he wants you to have. Strong words perhaps, but the touring market suffers particularly from a lack of specialist awareness. Most of the cycle trade responds to the fashions of the racing cyclist who, for all sorts of reasons, is less demanding. This is particularly true of frame builders, most of whom have a racing background.

Fortunately for cyclists there is growing

awareness of the engineering requirements of bikes, particularly of frame building. During the cycle boom of the mid-seventies, both here and in the United States, a number of engineer-builders started up, asking similar questions to those asked in this book. What we are trying to achieve is a better overall cycle trade, with our thoughts – and yours – fed back to the manufacturers for the benefit of all future customers.

1 Designing a Frame

The most important aspect of frame design is the fruitful two-way debate between builder and client. The whole process of formulating a conclusion – the frame of your dreams – is an iterative analysis and evaluation of each frame component, its material and its design. Apart from the actual cyclist, it is also important to analyse the purpose behind the frame. There are specialist frames made to cover a whole host of uses, with names like road racing, time trialing or testing, low profile (LP), cyclo-cross, track, criterium, touring, expedition, cycle-camping, rough-stuff, ATB or mountain, ATB racer, cycle speedway, clubmans, Audax or *randonnée*. Each has its individual hallmark and if a frame is required to do two or more tasks, a greater compromise will have to be accepted, compromise being a key word in good design.

Fig 1   A low profile, absolutely no good for touring.

Designing a quality frame set should not be regarded as a science (which should be applied in the workshop); it is an art, an art of compromise. If this were not true there would be tablets of stone instructing us precisely how each clone-like frame should be perceived. I said the process was iterative: you can start almost anywhere in your discussions but at some stage you will probably return and re-question decisions made earlier. That is a good sign of healthy progress.

I must stress that you should not go over the top when it comes to 'dimensioning' frames. There are limits of sensibility and most frame builders know where they lie. Some cyclists are obsessive about the minutest degree of detail and I have even heard of customers quoting toler-ance limits for the builder to meet. A good engineer is one who understands the relevance of each decision and its importance within the final requirement. The fact is that our bodies are tolerant of many dimensional inaccuracies and only a few aspects of frame building are actually very important. These aspects are: accurate tube mitring, complete and safe brazing, and the back wheel perfectly following the front. If the seat-tube angle is a quarter of a degree from ideal, your body will never know.

Do not misinterpret my attitude. I believe in attempting to get it right but I believe it is equally important not to forget the engineering reality of frame building; it is a process of fabrication worlds apart from the micrometers of machining.

Fig 2   Accurate tube mitring is a must for a quality frame.

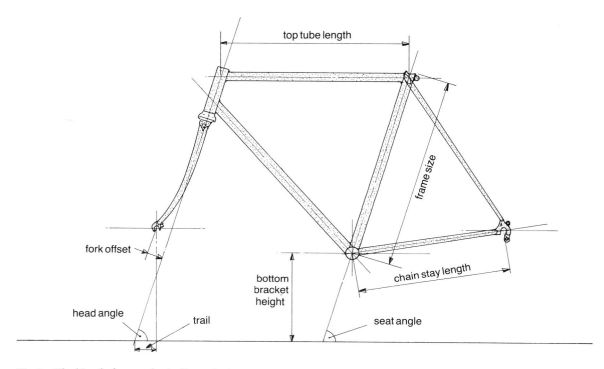

Fig 3   The bicycle frame – basic dimensions.

SEAT-TUBE ANGLE

This is the angle of the seat tube to the ground. It is conveniently measured as the angle between the seat tube and top tube but remember – not all top tubes are horizontal. Seat-tube angles are usually within the range of 70–75 degrees. Traditionally, 70–73 degrees is found on ATBs, 72–74 degrees for touring and 73–75 degrees for racing frames.

It is often thought that shallow seat-tube angles make for comfort and the more vertical it is the harsher but more efficient the ride. I am not wholly convinced, although I agree that this may be a true observation of bikes commonly found on the streets. However, the seat tube may only be secondary in creating this effect. The myth arises from the fact

that most bikes with shallow seat tubes have long wheelbases and use fat tyres, so giving more comfort, while all steep seat-tubed bikes are short, lively and use narrow uncomfortable tyres, hence the illusion arises from other factors. Custom builders produce comfortable touring frames with steep seat angles and, conversely, efficient racing designs with shallow seat angles when their client's body requires it so.

The main problem is how to determine what the seat angle should be. Many claim the centre of the knee-joint should be vertically above the pedal whilst on the forward stroke. Even though I have read in many so-called important publications that this single fact is paramount, I do not know why this is considered true and I have never found a satisfactory reason.

13

Fig 4   The knee should be vertically above the pedal (so some say).

This requirement was written in *Cycling* (CONI, Central Sports School, 1972), the reference book on road racing, but it does not say why. I am not sure how to find the centre of my knee-joint anyway. It is somewhere in the middle of my leg but where exactly? If I get it wrong my seat tube may be half a degree out!

In practice, my disbelief of the vertical knee position theory is borne out by the success of many human-powered vehicles (HPVs), where the athlete is in a sitting-down position (and so does not utilise gravity for aiding propulsion). The thought that gravity has anything to do with pushing power is hard to believe. As a consequence I find the value of a particular seat-tube angle difficult to determine. Since I do not believe the vertical-knee theory I use a different method. The relative positions of feet, hands and backside are of course important; too much energy can be wasted in attempting to sit in an unnatural position. Too shallow an angle causes the angle between your upper and lower body to be cramped, so leading to inefficient breathing. Too large

an angle will throw excessive weight on to your arms. Additionally, for the bike to handle properly, weight distribution must be correct. The normal accepted balance is 45 per cent on the front wheel and 55 per cent on the rear. For athletes with an abnormally high proportion of weight on their rear end, a steeper than standard seat angle will be the answer. Naturally the converse is true for athletes with extremely slender buttocks.

Over the last eight years I have concluded that seat angle is not especially important. An angle of 73 degrees has worked for most types of frame with few exceptions. After all, the vast majority of people are normally proportioned so far as the position of their knees is concerned (the interest here is in ratios and not absolute lengths). Increasing the seat angle by as little as half a degree will only move the saddle forward by 4mm. My solution is that, when designing, I start at around 73 degrees and I make adjustments based on body idiosyncrasies, weight distribution and the prospective uses of the frame.

HEAD ANGLE

The head angle is the angle the head tube makes with the ground. This angle has far more significance than the seat angle and so the choice should be detailed and accurate. It is, however, important to consider fork offset at the same time as the two dimensions are directly related.

Head angles vary from 69 degrees on ATBs to around 75 degrees on time trial bikes. The combination of head angle and fork offset will determine the steering characteristics of the bike. As a general principle, large fork offsets – often referred to as long fork rakes – go with shallow head angles for comfortable touring

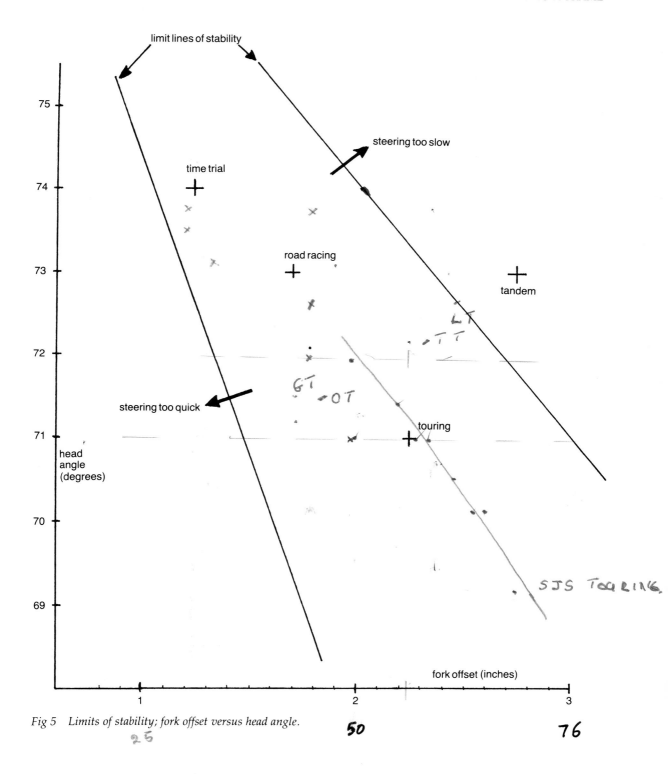

Fig 5   Limits of stability; fork offset versus head angle.

bikes. Small offsets and steep head angles are normally found on racing bikes, usually those maximised for speed and having little respect for comfort.

For any given head angle there is a range of acceptable fork offsets. If the rake is too long then the steering will appear sluggish, the bike will feel totally unresponsive and the handlebars oscillate on descents, especially when laden. If the rake is too short the steering will be so sensitive you will simply be dumped off the bike on the first rough-surfaced, twisting, steep, downhill road. For any given head angle it is as dangerous to have too great a fork offset as it is to have too small an offset.

The margin of safety is, however, not the same for all head angles. As the head angle increases the range of acceptable rakes reduces; so it is true to say that steering characteristics are much more sensitive to fork offset at steep head angles than at shallow head angles. A little known fact about steering geometry is that a shallow head angle can still be made to feel responsive if a suitable offset is chosen. Many believe a racing frame must have a 73 or 74 degree head angle in order to be acceptable. A fair mean-machine can still be built with a 72 degree head angle if the offset is kept in the region of 1¾in. It may be necessary to have a shallow head angle on a very small frame with a short top tube where toe-clip clearance from the front wheel is essential.

Traditional touring designs quote 72 degrees for the head. There appears to be no science behind this theory and it may be just a convenient solution. I have found a 71 degree head angle with 2⅛in–2¼in fork offset still gives a lively ride but is far more stable when laden, so reaching a much better compromise. Many of my customers are riding such machines and

are very happy with the combination. I have to work hard to persuade them to accept what seems such an old-fashioned angle but a quick spin on one of my test bikes usually clinches the decision.

I do not like to see 73 degree head angles on a touring machine. I know it is done but then I hear many murmurings about handlebar shimmer, especially with a handlebar bag and/or saddlebag. Similar reasoning leads me to conclude that conservative head angles should be considered for long-distance *randonnée* frames and club frames. It is a myth that steep angles produce a quicker mount. In fact you will need to be constantly vigilant, wasting energy trying to keep the bike directed. A self-steering, no fuss bike is such a delight when you are shattered.

A road racing bicycle must have responsive steering and must steer as the rider leans the bike. Tight formation riding within a bunch can be dangerous and it only needs one rider to topple a complete group. It is ideal if all road machines have similar steering characteristics. A bike with too much fork offset will be slower to turn than the rest in the bunch and a bike with too little offset will be too quick in changing course and be erratic in direction. Both scenarios can cause accidents.

When I build a road frame, I take location of riding into consideration. Many young, club riders have inherited a fetish for steep short-wheelbase bikes from ill-informed club-mates and an ill-informed Press. In North Wales, the local clubs regularly thrash over the high passes of Snowdonia and use the rougher roads on training rides. We are very fortunate to live in such countryside but the bike must do a lot more than that asked of it by a rider from the Fens where the roads are totally different. 74 degree head angles are considered steep around here and 75 degree heads are just a no go. A bike that handles properly can often outpace the theoretical masterpiece that proves too unstable downhill.

A tandem must have unique steering. It must steer only where the handlebars dictate. You do not want a tandem to self-steer (like a road frame) should either rider lean the machine. For example the stoker (rear rider) may lean to scratch his leg, tighten a toe-strap or just sway because of pedalling hard; the machine must not alter its line. Tandems, either touring or racing, must have similar head angles and fork offsets to be ridable. Steep head angles, 73 or 74 degrees, are required with longish fork offsets, typically between 2¼in and 2¾in.

On a solo this combination could be dangerous, leading to ferocious handle-bar oscillations whereas the tandem gets away with it due to its enormous wheel-base and the additional weight acting through the headset. The first racing tandem I built for myself had a 73 degree head angle and, mistakenly, only a 1¾in fork offset, a classic solo set-up. I, as a very experienced tandem pilot, had to battle to stay in a straight line. The machine wandered aimlessly between verge and white lines, especially when we got tired. The local club lads usually ended in the ditch. I built a new fork with 2½in offset and it now handles like a dream.

Tricycles too require neutral steering so that they do not steer as the machine leans. Tricycles are forever leaning, fol-lowing the cambers of our erratic roads but the rider requires it to go straight without a massive struggle. A classic road racing set-up would give you a perma-nent and unnecessary battle with the bars.

Fig 6   *Banana fork blades which are so popular in the UK. They are efficient but like a pneumatic drill.*

I have often read that a test of a good bike is how it rides with no hands on the handlebars. This is not always true. A bike designed with neutral steering – many touring or expedition bikes and all good tandems – should be extremely dif-ficult to ride no-hands as the steering is designed to be unaffected by leaning the machine. When riding no-handed, many bikes with this steering configuration will feel one-sided, since the minutest im-balance of weight distribution needs huge angles of lean as compensation. These bikes are also difficult to manoeuvre when being pushed by the saddle and attempting to steer by leaning. A racing solo should be very responsive to this

Fig 7 A sensibly small-radius fork rake for touring; gives lots of comfort.

treatment and a tandem should be totally unresponsive.

We have concluded that the amount of offset for a given head angle will determine the steering characteristics. However, there is more. The shape of the rake will determine the degree of comfort. Sadly, modern trends are going in favour of large radius banana-shaped fork blades. These may be fine for the time-trial rider who cycles for only a short period of time but most inappropriate for anyone who sits on the bike for more than a few hours. A blade with a small radius bend low-down near the fork-end will minimise the transmission of road vibrations through to the bars. To overcome modern, pneumatic-drill banana blades,

cyclists are expected to ride with thick foam, shock-absorbing pads either on the bars or on special cycling mitts – a strange solution to bad frame design. Fork blades are available from most tube manufacturers without a preformed rake. A good builder will then form the radius of rake most suited to your needs. Fashion unfortunately causes some dire compromises and many younger riders prefer to have numb hands rather than to be seen riding a fork that looks a little old-fashioned. It again depends on your priorities but I feel it is important to stress that the shape of the curve will have no effect on steering characteristics.

In this book, frame size is measured in the good old British way from the centre of the bottom bracket shell to the top of the seat tube. Frame size is again given considerable emphasis but varies with fashion, making hard and fast rules a nonsense. When I started to ride seriously at the end of the sixties, it was the fashion to ride as big a frame as you could get your leg over. Today the opposite is true and it is the vogue to have a lot of seat pillar protruding from the frame. It does not really matter that much how long your seat tube is and only you will know which fashion you wish to follow. I shall speak in general terms and point out that, normally, touring frames are larger than road frames. This is mainly due to the handlebar stem position, tourists usually wanting their bars higher than racing cyclists. A higher stem is better supported with the longer head tube of a larger frame.

This implies that the top tube is horizontal, which on some custom frames is not the case. To determine the correct frame size for you, I suggest you forget all those magic formulae and analyse your present frame size, fashion requirements and handlebar position, and decide on your compromise. Most cyclists going to a custom frame builder are already riding a fairly reasonable bicycle and are usually aware of how they wish their new machine to be. For the new rider or for those who believe they must be measured as part of the process of buying a custom frame, the standard equations are a good starting point. All these equations started from the *CONI* cycling book; even if you can measure yourself to the required accuracy, do not forget you will end up with an early seventies, Italian road racing frame set.

These *CONI* dimensions have little relevance in the touring world and

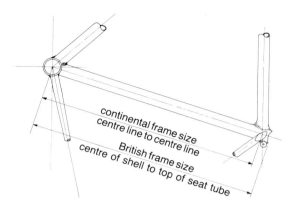

Fig 8   The two ways of measuring frame size. This book uses the British dimension, centre of bottom bracket to top of seat tube.

Fig 9   The classic racing set-up, high saddle and low handlebars; not exactly ideal for a camping tour.

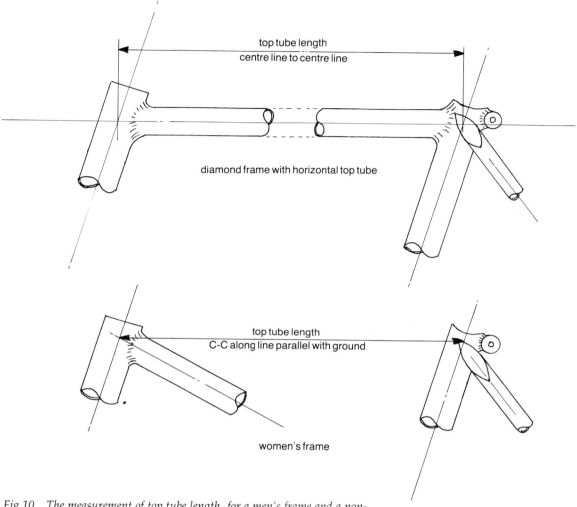

top tube length
centre line to centre line

diamond frame with horizontal top tube

top tube length
C-C along line parallel with ground

women's frame

Fig 10 The measurement of top tube length, for a men's frame and a non-horizontal top tube frame.

fashions have changed since their formulation. I do have a guide to sizing yourself for a touring frame but it should not be taken as gospel, nor should it be used for racing frames.

1. Top tube length is scientific and should be a function of the dimensions of your upper body and arm length. (The standard *CONI* route is quite acceptable but it does rely on your ability to find

obscure parts of your body and take accurate measurements.) I like to use a simpler method that also requires torso length and arm length but does not require you to find your pubis bone (the source of much amazement). However, you still need to find your sternum, acromion and wrist-fold. The torso is measured from your crotch to your sternum. The best way to measure this is to measure the distance from the floor to the top of your

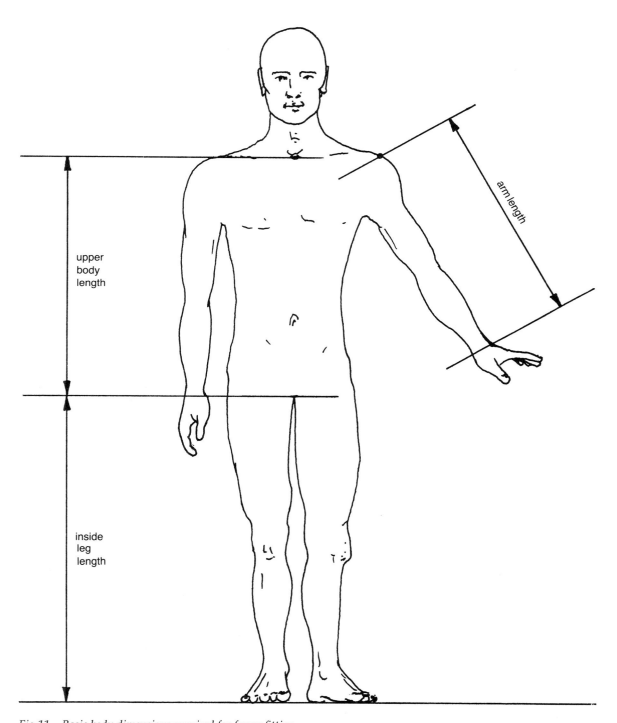

Fig 11   Basic body dimensions required for frame fitting.

Inside leg (in)	Frame size (in)	Crank length (mm)	Bracket height (in)
28	19	162.5	10⅛
29	19¾	165	10¼
30	20¾	165	10¼
31	21½	167.5	10⅜
32	22½	170	10½
33	23¼	170	10½
34	24¼	172.5	10⅝
35	25	175	10¾
36	26	175	10¾
37	27	177.5	10⅞
38	28	177.5	10⅞

Torso arm & body (in)	Top tube (in)	Stem length (mm)
39	20.0	60
40	20.2	70
41	20.4	75
42	20.6	80
43	20.8	90
44	21.0	90
45	21.3	95
46	21.6	95
47	21.9	100
48	22.2	100
49	22.5	105
50	22.9	105
51	23.4	110

Fig 12   Chart of recommended frame sizes.
This is a guide only and individual wants
should be taken into consideration.

sternum (the V in your collar bone just below your Adam's apple) and subtract your inside-leg measurement. This is best done with your back to a wall and in bare feet.

2. Measure your inside leg by placing a record album firmly up against your crotch, holding it square against the wall. Mark the wall, walk away and measure.

3. To measure your arm you will need help. The distance to be measured is from wrist-fold to acromion. Bend your hand back and the wrist-fold is where pivoting takes place. The upper body pivot (acromion) is the bony point on the back of your shoulder blade. Swing your arm to assist detection and then measure to the wrist-fold.

4. Add the distances for torso and arm and read off the recommended top tube length from Fig 12.

Do it a second time, with someone else holding the tape measure and I expect you will get a different answer. Do not worry too much because I only follow this guide to get an indication. In addition I like to analyse a cyclist's present riding position and make adjustments should they be necessary. A general finding is that most small- and medium-size frames are too long. The problem is exacerbated by the racing fraternity who want the fashionable looks of a very long handlebar stem: again fashion dictates over practicality and, again, often to the detriment of the riding position.

When relaxed on a bike, the hands should naturally fall on to the brake lever hoods. If the cyclist is constantly riding with the hands close to the centre of the bars, along the flat straight part, the reach is too long, caused by too long a top tube and/or too long a stem. This can go undetected if the bars are too low which itself gives the effect of an extended reach. The classic symptom is the rider never using the lower section of the drop handlebars as they feel uncomfortably distant.

If the bars are at the correct height and correct reach from the saddle it should be comfortable to use the drops, the brake lever hoods and the top of the bars. This not only gives more usable positions but alleviates aches and pains caused by being in the same position all day. Variety is a great help and one of the reasons honking (riding out of the saddle) uphill is so effective. Many cyclists find it necessary to move the brake levers higher up the bars. This again is a symptom of too long a reach and a better solution is to have the levers in their design position and shorten either frame or stem. Correctly positioned brake levers make very effective and comfortable handles when out of the saddle.

Varying the top tube length can affect other requirements. Both wheelbase and front centres will vary in sympathy and a short top tube can produce unacceptably short frames. The front centres, the distance between front wheel axle and bottom bracket axle, gives an indication as to whether or not toe-clips will overlap the front wheel. To some riders clearance here is imperative and in some countries it is law. It is a legal requirement, specified by the British Standard BS6102, that all mass-produced bikes sold in the UK have this clearance. Bicycles produced as one-offs, usually from custom builders, are exempt from BS6102: pedals may, within the law, overlap the tyre or mudguard.

If the clip must not foul the wheel or mudguard when cornering, short top tube frames must make other sacrifices and compromises by considering smaller wheels, shorter cranks, a steeper seat-tube angle and/or a shallower head-tube angle. All these items I feel are less important than the necessity to get the top tube length and handlebar reach correct. Inaccuracies in top tube fit can of course be corrected by altering the handlebar stem length. Quality stems vary in length from 6–14cm (2.4–5.5in), but it is imperative to attempt to get the frame right. I try

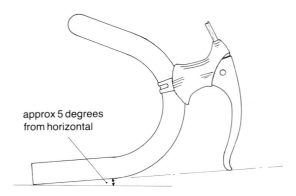

Fig 13 The approximate, correct position of the brake lever.

and build the smallest frames, say around 20in, to take a short stem of 6–7cm (2.4–2.8in) in length. Medium-size frames, 22in and thereabouts, look in good proportion with 9–10cm (3.5–4in) stems; and larger frames, 24in and above, often go in hand with 11cm (4.3in) stems or slightly longer. This is not a hard and fast rule and is something I discuss with my customers.

Incorrect top tube length is one of the single most common faults found on bicycles. I believe it is one of the most important dimensions of your bicycle and one of the most difficult to define. The standard *CONI* route gives a good indication for the racing cyclist. The tourist, however, usually needs a shorter top tube to give a slightly more upright riding position – a half to one inch usually works in practice.

BOTTOM BRACKET HEIGHT

If you are one of those cyclists compelled to pedal furiously around corners, go for a high bracket. Otherwise select a normal height of around 10⅝in with 170mm

23

cranks. If your cranks are longer put the bracket height up and if your cranks are shorter bring the height down. Vary the height according to Fig 12 on page 22 and then adjust this value according to your pedalling style. Those cyclists who never pedal around corners may require a lower bracket. The rough-stuff rider will want to increase the bracket height to give pedal clearance from rocks and ruts.

CHAIN STAY LENGTH

Is is commonly thought that chain stays should be short to minimise flex. It is true that short chain stays give a lively ride, (it actually appears that way because the steering feels more sensitive) but it is not true that long chain stays are in-efficient. The chain stay bridge, a tiny cross member behind the bottom bracket shell, does quite a lot of useful work. Regardless of how long the chain stays are, the distance from drop-out to bridge remains the same. The structure from bridge to shell is very solid, trapezoidal in format, and bend resistant. The only effective way to make chain stays stiffer is to use smaller wheels, such as 650bs, which will cause the bridge to rear drop-out distance to shorten by approximately one inch.

Chain stays tend to be around 17½–17¾in for touring bikes and 18in for expedition bikes. Again it is all a matter of compromise, a debate between handling, luggage to foot clearance and excessive wheelbase. Other restrictions are placed upon the builder when unusual frame tube sets are used for touring. The 753, 653 and many Columbus racing sets do not have long enough chain stays to allow anything beyond 17in. A decision must then be made as to which

is more important, design or available materials.

DROP-OUT WIDTH

The distance between fork-ends on both front fork and rear drop-outs is known as the drop-out width. For front forks, the standard is 100mm between faces. Most front hubs are made to this dimension but some cheap hubs are still 94mm although they are losing favour (a few spacing washers can always be added). A few racing, mainly low-profile bikes use a narrow 80mm hub, but this is not recom-mended for the tourist. Tandems have an additional standard hub width of 110mm but they have not caught on in the UK. This is a pity as the more spread the hub flanges, the more support the rim gets to side loadings. Some tandems with front hub brakes use 126mm, but these are one-offs.

Rear drop-outs are obtainable in several widths: 120mm, 126mm, 130mm, 135mm and 140mm. The 126mm is the most com-mon and usually recommended: it is ver-satile and the hubs can be redished to build strong wheels. 130mm is a favourite with ATB riders and 140mm for tandem-ists. 120mm is an old dimension found on what was known as five-speed hubs. Few hubs today will fit these narrow frames but the spacing washers can always be altered if necessary.

Shimano have recently introduced eight-speed freehubs which need a 130mm frame spread. Close behind (not wishing to be outdone) Regina of Italy offer a 130mm spaced, conventional eight-speed hub and block set – their Synchro-Silver 90–S. If your fork-ends are 120mm or 126mm apart, do not be tempted to spring the backend to fit such wide hubs. The extra stresses cause prem-

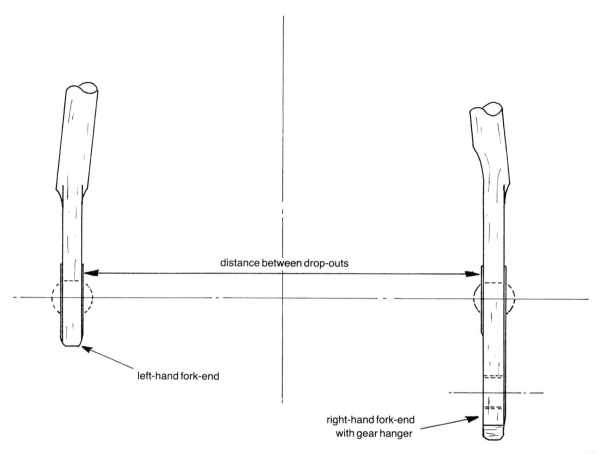

distance between drop-outs

left-hand fork-end

right-hand fork-end
with gear hanger

Fig 14   Rear view of rear fork-ends showing the measurement of drop-out width.

ature fork-end failure. Believe you me, this type of fatigue breakage is quite common and exceedingly annoying when it happens on tour.

Details of hub widths and dishing is given in the section on wheels. I suggest you choose the drop-out width to match your wheel requirements.

WHEELBASE

This is a dimension which is really quite

irrelevant, but one so many cyclists are obsessed with. If all other dimensions are accurately and correctly assessed, the wheelbase can be nothing but predetermined. It should never be a prerequisite dictating other decisions. It is something I rarely measure at design stage or even after construction. I am afraid to say that the debate about wheel-bases only highlights the lack of attention given to the real and important questions of frame design.

2 Materials

We have more or less gone through the design questions. Next we must consider the materials. This is where the world of science creeps in: modern frame materials owe a lot to technology. The leader in hi-tech steels was Reynolds with their 753, a steel fifty per cent stronger than their popular 531 metal. Lost wax investment castings, an expensive process for producing quality crowns, lugs and shells, has dramatically improved frame fittings.

I shall not be talking about alloy, carbon fibre or titanium frames. At this stage, there is so much going for steel that these alternatives are a bit of a joke when it comes to custom building. When the alternatives first appeared, steels were put under pressure and had to fight back. They did so and three major tube manu-facturers, Reynolds, Columbus and Tange, now offer some very hi-tech steels with energy-efficient, high-yield stresses and superior fatigue resistances.

A bicycle frame is built from a set of eleven pipes, a set of lugs, fork-ends, fork crown, bottom-bracket shell, bridges and a brazing medium. It takes many hours of hard sweat and loving care to create a machine of which you can be proud. Choice and permutations of mixes are endless. After all, that is why you go to a custom builder – to get something a bit special.

TUBE CHOICE

British cyclists are paranoid about light-ness. I do not know why this is so, but I try to convince them that a frame needs to be efficient and that does not necessarily mean that it has to be the lightest. A little extra thickness to some frame tubes can dramatically increase stiffness and life expectancy. A heavy main triangle will give particularly efficient hill climbing, yet if the forks and stays are reasonably light the frame will remain nimble and exciting.

Historically, Reynolds frames (the old ones with the 531 double-butted trans-fers) were not that well balanced. The forks had massive overkill and the main triangles were rather thin. Most crashed 531 frames have crumpled top and down tubes with the forks remaining perfectly true. Columbus have always worked the other way, heavy main tubes with light forks, great for hill work. Their crashed frames are cheaply repaired with a new fork. Since those days, Reynolds have revamped their range and now produce some excellent tube sets, 531c being a classic example of good balance through-out at a competitive price.

Most UK tourists choose Reynolds 531. For the majority of cases this selection is perfect but for optimum performance there may be alternatives. If Reynolds and Columbus tubes were exactly the same there would be no debate. Luckily they are not and this allows greater scope to individualise your frame. There are two main aspects to consider: the gauge of the tube (its thickness); and the mechanical properties of the steel. The latter is a bit more technical and looks at the relative strengths and stiffnesses of the different

Fig 15   Classic front-end crash of the old-fashioned Reynolds 531db tubing.
The overkill forks are perfect but the down and top tubes have bent.

steels used in 531, 653, 753, Columbus Nivacrom, Columbus CrMo Cyclex, Tange Prestige and so on.

Most frames are built from a tube set obtained from one or other of the known manufacturers. Each set has its own distinguishing transfer so the customer knows exactly what he is buying. Many custom builders use standard sets but many deviate on occasions to produce a totally individual frame. Reynolds appreciate this and so they have produced a special transfer set, 531 Designer Select. It is only available to the very small individualistic builders, a recognition of what we actually do and, I think, a nice touch.

As a starting point I will list standard frame sets, roughly grouped into three classifications: very heavy for camping and expeditions; medium for general touring, the odd camp, and for weekends away; and light for Audax, club riding and the occasional hostel weekend. I am not considering racing use and I shall leave Reynolds 753 and its relevance to touring until last.

Heavy Use

This group includes Reynolds 531 Super Tourist and Columbus SP and SPX. All three sets have a lot in common, in particular their main triangles which all use

27

0.7/1.0mm butted tubes. The 531 set has thicker forks (those of the old-fashioned 29mm × 16mm oval) for which good cast crowns are limited to two flat-top models – perfectly adequate but not fashionable. All Columbus sets use the wider oval of 28mm × 19mm, compatible with a huge range of quality crowns. The 531 set comes with slightly longer chain stays, the longest possible with standard Columbus stays and vertical fork-ends being 17½in. The SPX option is claimed to offer benefit from five helical ribs inside the seat and down tubes and straight ribs in the chain stays. I do not believe they offer much but they are a great way of being one-up. Standard Columbus SP and SPX sets come with 14mm seat stays although, of heavy gauge, the 16mm

option from Columbus or Reynolds is worth substituting.

Christine, my wife, rides a Columbus SPX touring frame. It is the stiffest frame she has had, quick on the hills yet not uncomfortable.

Medium Use

The medium group contains only a few tube sets, Columbus SL and SLX, and Vitus GTI. Reynolds do not have a set of equivalent weight, their 531 Super Tourist being too heavy and their 531 Competition too light.

I am not a great lover of the Columbus SLX: it has identical internal reinforcements as the SPX but the tubing is sufficiently thin to give me concern. Each

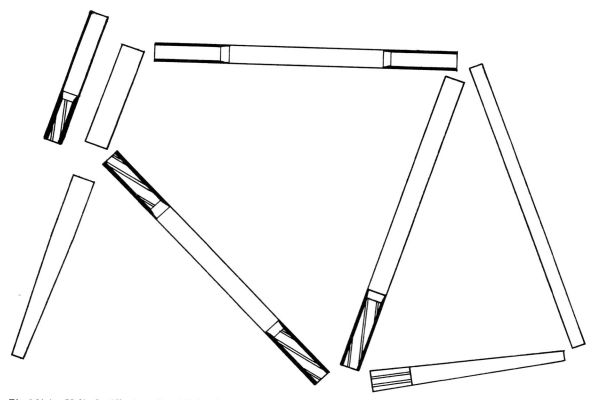

Fig 16(a)   Helical stiffening ribs of Columbus SLX, SPX and TSX.

Fig 16(b)

reinforcing rib has two potential stress raisers, not a problem on SPX because the tubing is much thicker. Stress raisers form the roots from which fatigue cracks grow. Columbus SL is, in my opinion, a much better buy, even though it is regarded as a down-market brother of SLX. In this group, Vitus GTI with its stiff, triple-butted format is perhaps the best of the three. It is one of those unknown sets that deserves more favour. I have great difficulty in selling its merits simply because Vitus is not a name recognised for its steels. Their butting profiles are pro-gressive and the quality of their steel is high.

Light Use

The light group contains Reynolds 531 Competition, 653, 700 and 708 Classic, Columbus TSX and Vitus TXO. For reasons similar to those mentioned on the SLX, I am not keen on the TSX; even less so since the tubing has helical ribs on its thinnest central sections. Reynolds have approached rib-style stiffening with much more style; their 700 Classic series has a round external section and a rounded square internal shape. This has been superseded by their eight-sided version, 708. Stress raisers are eliminated and the resulting tube is (or is claimed

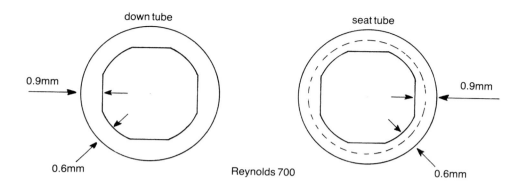

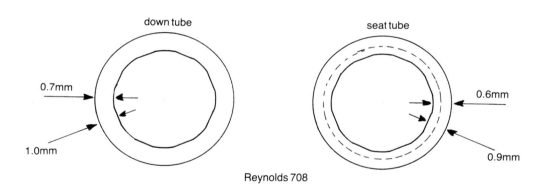

Fig 17   Cross-section of Reynolds 700 and 708 main tubes.

to be) stiffer than the round equivalent as long as it is brazed in the correct orientation.

In this group Reynolds 531 Competition must represent the best value, much better than their 653. It is a poor man's 753 offering neither the strength nor overall stiffness. It has identical gauges to 753 which I believe to be inadequate for the slightly inferior material. 531 Competition offers a better and longer-lasting frame. Even so, 653 has gained a large following so I shall say no more.

As you have probably realised there is not a lot of choice, especially within the medium group. This is precisely where true custom frames come into their own. Mixes can be devised where some tubes are Columbus, some Reynolds and some Vitus. This is where delicate balances are made resulting, I hope, in brilliant, practical and enjoyable frames. I have attempted to illustrate this point by listing tubes in weight order, mixing all makes, as shown in Appendix III.

It is clear from the seat-tube listing that

Reynolds only make two in 531. Between them are a whole array of alternatives and it is the seat tube that I usually change in a Reynolds frame. The heavy 1.0/0.7mm seat tube is often too heavy while the 0.8/0.55mm seat tube is nearly always too light. For many frames, I recommend a gauge of tube between the two, Vitus GTI (0.9/0.7/0.6mm) or Columbus SL (0.9/0.6mm). I usually try to persuade my customers to accept this change even in a road-racing format. A Vitus GTI seat tube in particular gives the bottom bracket area a much more solid feel, being triple- and heavier-butted. I do not do this without the customer's approval but their feedback suggests it is well worth while.

From the listings, one for each tube, you can select your combination of ideals. The permutations are huge, so I have listed a few of my favourites (*see* Appendix IV) and below I have commented on a few of the individual tubes of particular interest.

For heavy touring use I generally use 1.0mm Columbus head tubing, it being a little thicker than the 0.9mm equivalent from Reynolds. Columbus SP and OR fork blades are often substituted as they produce a wonderful compromise of dimensions. They are strong enough for touring yet not too heavy to be uncomfortable. They complement Columbus SL and other tube sets in the medium-weight range. The OR blade is slightly thicker by 0.05mm and if just one fork blade had to be chosen as an ideal touring fork, I would choose this one. I rarely use Reynolds 531 Competition seat tubes, even on racing frames. As I said earlier, I consider them a little thin and I prefer Columbus SL or Vitus GTI seat tubes. Frames benefit from extra stiffness between bottom bracket and front-gear mechanism so the chain does not rub when pedalling hard – a problem associated with thin, bendy seat

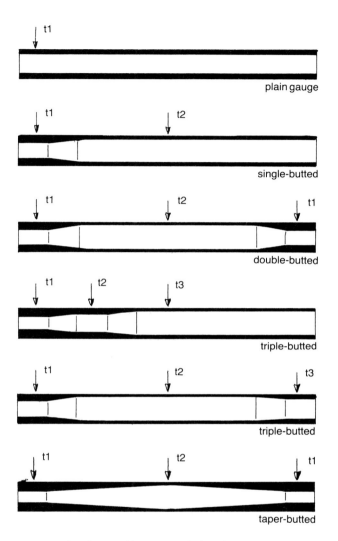

Fig 18   Butting profiles commonly found in quality main tubes.

tubes. 531 Competition seat tubes have an annoying habit of wanting a 27.4mm seat pillar. Columbus SL and Vitus GTI seat tubes have slightly thicker walls allowing a standard 27.2mm seat pillar.

I often replace 531 Competition top tubes with Vitus GTI or Columbus SL alternatives. Again they are just that little bit heavier being stiffer and more resistant to denting – dented top tubes being amazingly common on club and touring bikes. Substitution of both top and seat tubes in a 531 Competition set is, in effect, giving a frame similar in tube dimensions to the Columbus SL. The substitution is necessary because Reynolds do not make 531 top and seat tubes in 0.6/0.9mm gauges. I often use heavy Reynolds 531 Super Tourist 16mm seat stays when cantilever or braze-on centre-pull brakes are being used. The larger diameter and thicker gauge resists the torque reaction of the mounting pivots better. For heaviest use, tandems and expedition bikes, I use the new ATB seat stays from Reynolds (the double taper 19mm variety). They are massive, and excellent for mounting brakes and the kitchen sink!

REYNOLDS 753

Reynolds 753 was the first heat-treated super steel to hit the market over ten years ago. Since that time the material specification has improved and tube gauges changed. Initially the 753 had rather thin tubes and consequently there were limitations on its use. The rumours suggested 753 was bendy and fragile; I do not believe there was much evidence then but it definitely is not true now. The modern 753 (a derivative of 753R) is thicker and in my opinion sufficient for general touring; heavy cycle-camping may be pushing your luck but it is absolutely ideal for hostelling, club and Audax riding. Other gauges of 753 are now available from the 753 Tandem and 753 all-terrain tube sets. Individual tubes for mixes are not easy to obtain from Reynolds, but it is not impossible.

It is often thought that the strength and stiffness of 753 makes for an uncomfortable ride. This is not so: a piece of 753 bends just like a piece of 531 but when it bends it does not require energy to bend it back again. That is the basic reason why 753 is so good. When you load it hard, thrashing uphill, it does not absorb energy – energy that should be making you go forward. To explain this phenomenon it is necessary to delve into a bit of physics. The stiffness of a material is defined by its Young's modulus. However, the Young's modulus for different alloys of steel does not vary greatly. This implies that all steels, the chrome-molybdenums from Vitus and Columbus or the manganese-molybdenums from Reynolds, have identical bending properties. Yet this is only true within the confines of a laboratory. A frame is a complex three-dimensional structure where kinetic modulus is the buzz word.

For example, as we bend a top tube sideways, the tube's outer face will be stretched, the inner face compressed and the top and bottom faces left alone. If parts of the inner or outer faces are stressed too much, small amounts of the metal may be taken beyond the yield point of the metal. Yield points vary considerably between the steels of various Reynolds and Columbus tubes. The higher the yield point, the more difficult it is for the tube to enter this inefficient regime – the area of micro-yielding. Going beyond the yield point is energy absorbing because work must be done to return the tube back to its prior position, this work being called strain-absorption. So a high-yield-point steel tube will bend just like a lower-yield-point version, but it will absorb less energy in doing so. This gives the ultimate in efficiency and comfort.

Within small loadings there is no advantage to hi-tech steels. A six-stone weakling twiddling low gears will get little or no benefit from such tubing. The only advantage of 753 is where and when the tube would otherwise micro-yield, when pushed to extremes. A pair of track tandem riders, or a cycle-camper grovelling up Bwlch-yr-Groes will be penalised if they use anything other than a material of the quality of 753. The question of how much better, or stiffer, or even more efficient, 753 is over and above 531 cannot be answered. It is often quoted that 753 is fifty per cent stronger; that is true but this number does not necessarily indicate how much more efficient 753 is. This depends so much on how hard the tube is being asked to work. Even when pushed to its absolute limit only parts of the tube's sections are micro-yielding with bending forces. Torque forces affect the whole of a tube's cross-section but the conclusion based on an average of the two is that 753 is between zero and fifty per cent better than 531, depending on how much you push it – in other words I do not know.

The main cause of tube failure is fatigue, continuous back and forward oscillating forces such as those caused by road vibration and pedalling. This property is difficult to quantify as the probability of fatigue failure is very dependent on the design of the tube/lug interface, as well as material properties and the degree of cyclic loadings. A good indication of material resistance to fatigue can be taken from its yield point since fatigue proceeds by the yielding of material local to the tip of the discontinuity. A material, such as 753, with a high-yield point is therefore more resistant to local yielding, cracks being slow to mature. In simple words, it does not break so easily.

Heat-treated steels such as 753 are vulnerable in the workshop. If heated too long, too many times or at too high a temperature, the superior qualities of the material may vanish. The actual dependence on time and temperature is complex and there are no specific rules or guide-lines. The ultimate quality of your 753 frame is therefore at the mercy of your frame builder. It is for this reason that Reynolds introduced the test, a destructive test, where the brazer submits a sample joint for in-depth analysis. Even so some brazers are so good that the test reveals negligible damage to the quality of the material whilst with others, a small but acceptable loss of properties is detected. The worst that can happen is the material reverting to 531.

The main drawback of 753 is the cost. The basic tube set is much more expensive than 531 and it must be constructed with silver brazing materials. These are frightfully expensive, making a significant contribution to the total cost. 753 will only exhibit its true qualities if it is constructed to exacting standards with top-class components, lugs, shells, etc. Cheaply made 753s are not always good value, so take a bit of care in selection. For the tourist there are a few problems as 753 cannot be cold set and the fork blades come pre-set to a racing style rake. The offset is long enough for most touring forks but the shape is not ideal. 753 chain stays are only racing length and it is impossible to design long, stable, rear ends.

The only other problem is with silver-brazing. This process is necessary as it operates at a low temperature which is imperative for the tubing to maintain its strength. However, fluxes for these low-temperature brazing mediums are hygroscopic – they absorb moisture from the air – causing permanent damp. If insufficient flux is used during construction, silver penetration of the lugged joint may not be complete. Too much flux and long-term corrosion may set in, arising from the sludge left inside the tube. This is a particular problem for tourists as they

Fig 19   753 with an extended seat tube for lightness and strength.

tend to ride all winter and in awful conditions.

To alleviate internal corrosion, care should be exercised during construction and flux removed from inside the open tubes wherever possible. The top tube, fork blades and seat stays should be sealed, which means oxidation will cease as soon as all the oxygen is used up within the air gap of the tube. The main joints concerned are the down tube to head tube and the fork-ends into chain stays.

I conclude that hi-tech tubes are most beneficial if you work your bike hard. Buy the best steels you can afford and compromise this decision with other factors such as tube diameter and gauge. Col-

umbus have introduced a new range of steels, Nivacrom and Cr-Mo Cyclex. Nivacrom is close to 753 in properties, as is Tange Prestige, and all should be treated with respect in order to benefit fully from their charms. Cr-Mo Cyclex steel is similar in specification to 653 and considerably better than 531, which is getting a little left behind these days. Cr-Mo Cyclex is used on all the standard Columbus range which makes the likes of their SP, SL and their helical versions, TSX, SPX and SLX even more desirable. They offer 653 steel strengths but in sensibly thicker gauges.

Appendix II lists tensile strengths of all the common steels used in quality frames. Unfortunately this data alone does not give a true representation of relative efficiencies of the steels. Yield stresses are only quoted for Vitus steels but one can generally assume that yield points would form a similarly ordered list. This assumes similar brazing techniques for each steel. Tubes lose fewer of their properties if brazing temperatures are kept down as low as possible. In simple terms, carefully made frames are more efficient particularly with the higher quality steels.

I do have favourites: I like Reynolds 753 and 531c, Columbus SL, SP and SPX; and I particularly like Vitus GTI. Each have different roles to play and between them they cover a lot of ground. Reynolds 531 used to be the standard all others were judged by. It is still very good but it is getting a bit long in the tooth; for instance, Columbus SL metal is now 28 per cent stronger and more efficient than 531 metal.

I do not intend to tell you which tubing you should use, simply because there are too many permutations to cover. That is up to you and your builder to thrash out, but I hope I have got you thinking along new lines – there being more to today's steels than the colour of the transfer.

FRAME COMPONENTS

Investment casting, via a lost-wax process, has brought true quality to bicycle frames. The process is able to produce accurate and complex shapes and all made from very superior materials. Cinelli is the name synonymous with cast components. They deserve recognition for being leaders in educating cyclists to their benefits. However, many manufacturers now offer investment cast frame parts and in many cases other makes may be more suited to your frame.

BOTTOM BRACKET SHELLS

It is often said that the bottom bracket shell is the heart of the frame. It is a focal point where four tubes meet, it houses the crank axle and it is highly stressed. Cast shells are marketed by Bertoli, Bocama, Cinelli, Columbus, Eisho, Everest, Haden, Ishiwata, Mazzuccato, Reynolds, Saba, Silva, Takahashi, Tange and Vitus, to name but a few! With perhaps one exception they are all as good as Cinelli but they are all without doubt better than cheaper bulge-formed or pressed shells.

I consider good threads a most important property which the shell must have. Quite a number of frames come for repair because the bottom bracket threads have stripped. These all have non-cast shells where the weaker metal fails with time. Accuracy of thread alignment is important as this may affect longevity of the bottom bracket bearings. It is also important that the faces of the shell are machined absolutely square to each other after the shell is brazed. There can be distortion during manufacture and should the faces not be square, the bottom bracket cups may seat out of line.

Fig 20   Investment cast bottom-bracket shell. The process is ideal for complex shapes, in this case on a Vitus Arcor aero frame.

Figs 21 and 22 show the difference between two bottom-bracket shells, one micro-cast and the other welded. The latter has considerable metal missing at the weld, so much so the threads are non-existent. This shell generally has shallow threads and is destined for the bin. A further advantage of cast shells is the accuracy of formation of the frame tube sockets. A precise fit between tube and socket produces a stronger bond, especially when silver brazing the joint. Silver brazing mediums are extremely strong if the gap between tube and lug is within a small range – around three-thousandths of an inch. Silver is not a strong metal when spread over large gaps.

The argument is similar for super glues. They work marvellously if the break is clean and does not require large gaps to be filled. Lost-wax casting can provide great accuracy but this in turn creates prob-

Fig 21   *Quality threads are associated with investment cast shells.*

Fig 22   *Disgusting threads on a dustbin-bound bulge formed bottom-bracket shell.*

lems. A shell is made in one specific format, one angle between down and seat tubes and another angle between seat tube and chain stay. A Cinelli shell, for example, is made for a seat-tube to down-tube angle of 60.5 degrees. Should your frame geometry be different you may have problems as this angle can only be varied by about one degree. You could, if desperate, grind metal away or, by inserting long poles, distort the shell to your requirements. I do not see the point as other makes of shells are made in other angles. Vitus shells, for example, suit small-angled frames. Bertoli and Everest make shells in a range of angles giving the ultimate in choice.

The process of investment casting is such that it is difficult to create very thin sections. Most cast shells have walls 1–1.5mm thick at their tips. For super-thin frame tubing such as 653 and Columbus Record (now obsolete but still about) I feel shells with thinner socket tips are more appropriate. Fatigue life of stressed areas is dependent on interface design. As an example, Columbus Record has plain gauge tubes 0.5mm thick. A cast shell with a 1.0mm wall thickness will create a sectional step from 0.5mm to 1.5mm at the shell's interface. This 3:1 ratio is well outside recommended limits for fatigue-resistant joints. For very thin tubing, shells should ideally be much thinner. It is not only impractical to thin a cast shell, it would also be very time consuming (the metal being extremely hard). For these rare occasions a non-cast shell can be better. You can obtain ones with good threads and made from quality steel. One is the RGF as shown in Fig 25, in this case brazed into a frame of 753T tubing.

For touring, this debate is hardly necessary – tubes are much thicker. I purposely omitted 753 from the list of dubious combinations. As a material, 753 exhibits

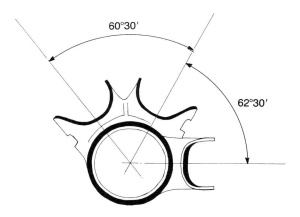

Fig 23   Cinelli investment cast, bottom-bracket shell and angular dimensions.

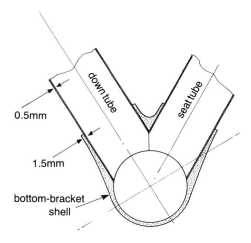

Fig 24   Cross-section of cast shell with thin (Columbus Record 0.5mm) tubes. Note the 3:1 step ratio change at lug end. This will lead to premature fatigue breakage.

better fatigue resistance, so it can cope with greater step changes than lesser tubes of the same gauge.

LUGS

The strength of a lugged joint does not come from the lug but the bond between

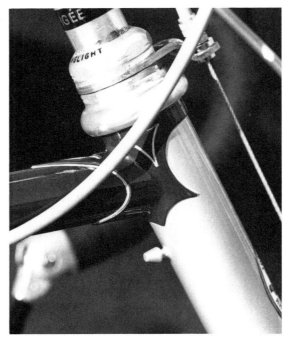

Fig 26   *A bit of filing and a standard lug can be made very attractive. This one started as a Prugnat I4.*

Fig 25   *A quality non-investment cast shell, necessary with some very thin tube sets, here with Reynolds 753T.*

the tubes' mating surfaces. This is only true if the tubes are precision mitred and the lug is full of brazing medium in which case the lug can be regarded as a cosmetic means of holding the glue in place.

A well-designed and thinned lug will also help distribute stresses away from the joint – but that is about all it does. This is why I consider cast lugs a luxury: they have little to offer structurally if the frame is built properly. I prefer to build with cast lugs as their accuracy saves time and less brazing medium is required. They are expensive and not many are suitable for laid-back touring angles, most being for 74 and 75 degree head and seat angles.

Fig 27   *An investment-cast bottom head lug. This is from Takahashi and is suitable for touring angles.*

Takahashi make an excellent set suiting a medium-size touring frame, as shown in Fig 27.

Frame top tubes tend to be rather thin. Cast lugs have relatively thick tangs (the bits that form the points). These are difficult to thin, being of such hard steel and of such a complicated shape. As with cast bottom-bracket shells the problem is again fatigue failure at the interface. Cast lugs and thin tubes should be mated with extreme caution. Cast lugs are ideal for the touring mount where frame gauges are comparable. It is a sad observation that the reverse is practised: cast lugs are predominantly found on lighter racing frames.

Pressed lugs are pretty good today. Their poor quality ten to twenty years ago has been used as an argument for the use of cast lugs. Prugnat and Bocama make an excellent range of quality thin-walled lugs in many angles and designs. These can be further worked on to create some very fancy shapes should that be your fetish. I personally like a plain lug which done neatly has a classic look.

I hope I have shown that lug choice is personal, so go for whichever design you like the look of. Structurally they are all equal although I have heard some builders say cut-out lugs help to ensure complete filling of the joint. Prugnat make an extensive range with short or long points, with or without cut-outs. Bocama points are medium length, again with or without cut-outs.

Lugless frames are necessary on occasions where sizes and angles are so extreme neither lugs nor bottom-bracket shells can be found to fit. Some cyclists prefer the clean look of a lugless bike and consequently ask for such frames. Structurally there is little between a lugged and lugless joint. In practice, however, the story is different. There are two aspects of

Figs 28 and 29   Two views of Takahashi cast lugs on a 71 degree head touring frame.

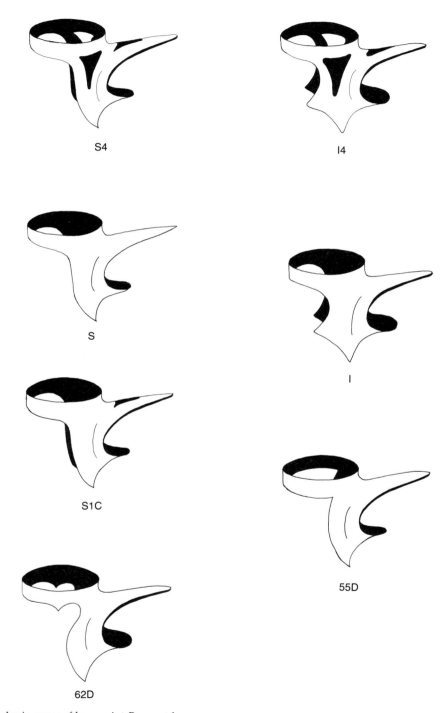

Fig 30   *The basic range of long point Prugnat lugs.*

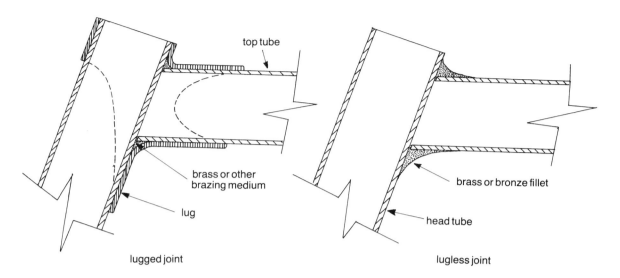

Fig 31 Cross-section of a lugged and lugless joint.

lugless construction that concern me; both are indirectly related to the fillet brazing technique and are long-term related problems associated with the fitting of headset and seat pillar.

I will expand the head tube argument in the section on tandem head tubes because this is where most of the problems occur. I shall just advise you to look out for any old Higgins Ultralight trikes – most were lugless and all are now getting old. Many I have seen have bulging head tubes, just around the area the headset is fitted. A headset is a tight press-fit into the head tube and in time, helped by vibration and riding stresses, the thin, non-reinforced head-tube metal will creep.

The case against lugless seat-tube joints is similar. Seat tubes are thin (one of the thinnest parts of many frames) so when heated will distort. Lugless brazing, in particular, distorts the seat tube as brazing is only on one side of the tube. A lug requires heat to be applied all round the tube so it distorts uniformly back into a circle. My concern is reaming, a process of

Fig 32 Lugless brazing is necessary for unusual situations. Here, fork blades have been used as chain stays to give more tyre clearance on a rough-stuff frame.

41

Fig 33   Two quality cast-fork crowns – a Takahashi on the left and a Bocama on the right.

removing internal metal from the tube so the seat pillar is an exact fit. The seat tube walls are very thin and cannot afford to have much metal taken off by a reamer. A lugged joint has the lug and brazing metal to back it up, so any reaming that is necessary has little chance of causing weakness.

For the lugless brazing of oversize top tubes on tandems, trikes and expedition bikes (necessary if oversize lugs are not available) it pays to sleeve the seat tube with a modified lug or a special. This is common on tandems and is referred to as semi-lugged construction. It minimises distortion and reinforces the thin seat tube, but it is expensive as it takes a lot more time.

I have nothing against lugless techniques at points where reaming does not take place, such as the bottom-bracket

shell or the cross-over points of tandem lateral tubes. If lugless head tubes are required then I recommend you use over-size head tubing or semi-lugged methods as detailed in the tandem section on pages 86–90.

FORK CROWNS

I believe cast fork crowns to be as essential as a good bottom-bracket shell. After all, unlike a lug, it has structural functions. Again the most famous name is Cinelli but there are equivalent, better and often more suitable models from other manufacturers such as Bertoli, Bocama, Columbus, Everest, Haden, Ishiwata, Mazzuccato, Reynolds, Saba, Silva, Takahashi, Tange and Vitus.

Again, choice depends very much on

style but you must also consider the width you require and the dimensions of the oval fork blades you are going to use. All Columbus and Reynolds standard forks use the wide oval of 28 × 19mm, except Reynolds 531 Super Tourist blades which still use the dated oval of 29 × 16mm. There are only a few good crowns still available for these latter blades, the flat top Cinelli MR, Bocama's Super Luxe and Haden's Europa. The wide oval choice is endless, giving good reason to select Columbus touring blades, even on a 531ST frame.

FORK-ENDS

I am an out and out fan of vertical fork-ends. They look neater, they make wheel removal a delight, they stop the wheel pulling over, but they are not easy to braze into the frame. Sceptics say you cannot move your wheel to one side should a spoke break. My answer to them is to read this book (*see* pages 101–19 on wheels) because there are ways of building bullet-proof wheels. You can, of course, carry a spoke key so that in the event of a spoke breaking you can make slight adjustments until you get somewhere to implement a better repair.

I shall exclude Campagnolo vertical fork-ends from these discussions as they are so inferior, being nothing more than a flat plate. The best ones are made by Suntour, Shimano and Takahashi, closely followed by Columbus and Tecnociclo.

A significant advantage of verticals is that they all have short tangs (the flat bit that protrudes forward and is brazed into the chain stay). Short tangs make the rear triangle considerably stiffer: a flat plate being far more flexible than the round section of a chain stay. The builder can feel this to be so. Fork-end alignment

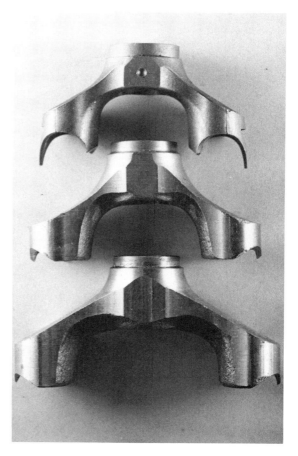

Fig 34   Three fork crowns of different widths. The top is for standard road use, the middle for a city bike and the bottom is full-width for a mountain bike.

tools are fitted to the ends and gently heaved upon to ensure the two fork-end faces are exactly parallel. With long tang road-ends there is a lot of flexibility. However, a solid vertical end can cause quite a sweat!

Road-ends have one advantage – their gear hangers are shorter (that is the distance from the wheel axle to the hole into which the gear screws). The quality of gear change depends on how far the gear mechanism's top jockey wheel is from the

Fig 35   Shimano SF22 vertical fork-end set. Ideal for serious touring but not so easy to braze into the frame.

block's sprockets. If you are using close ratio blocks then you may gain advantage by using a short drop road-end. This may even be necessary with some models of index gearing. Road-ends are now all short. Those long Campagnolo 1010 ends of years ago have gone, thank goodness. A short road-end is quite adequate and many are now available with mudguard eyes, some even have two (for carrier and guard). Most models from respected names will last, but be cautious of thin-looking ones.

Front fork-ends are all very much the same. Choice here is between those that have one, two or no mudguard eyes.

SEATS

Seat-stay bridges are now quite hi-tech, the latest being investment cast and quite

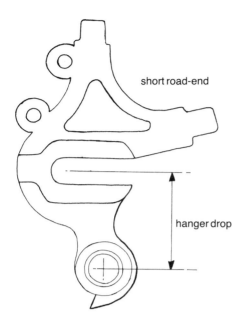

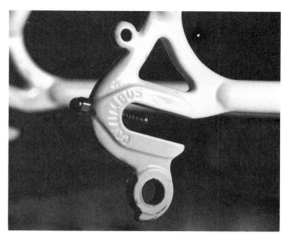

Fig 37 *A modern, short road-end with mudguard eyes. This Columbus model has a shorter gear hanger drop than a vertical fork-end.*

attractive. I always use these on racing frames but the tourist with braze-on brakes requires something quite simple. Usually 14mm 531 tubing makes good sense here and little reinforcing diamonds are often brazed to their ends, against the seat stays. Similarly with chain stay bridges: racing designs are amazing but unsuitable for the tourist, who normally wishes to clip on a mudguard.

Seat-pin bolts are either Allen bolt accessories for lugs having ears or recessed Allen key-bolt fittings. There is little difference structurally between the two, especially on a good frame with a correctly fitting seat pillar. If the fit is second rate, excessive pressure will be put on the lug's ears and the bolts. This will give long-term hassle so it is a problem best eliminated when new. Metals creep with time, particularly brass, and a lot of seat bosses become distorted over the years simply because the seat pillar has been too small. A properly fitted seat pillar can be held tight without recourse to violence: the reverse side to normal of the Allen

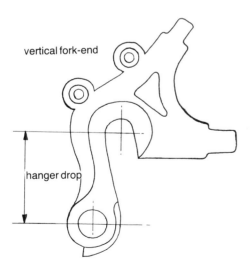

Fig 36 *Rear fork-ends and hanger depth. Short drop hangers are better with close ratio blocks; deep hangers for large rear sprockets.*

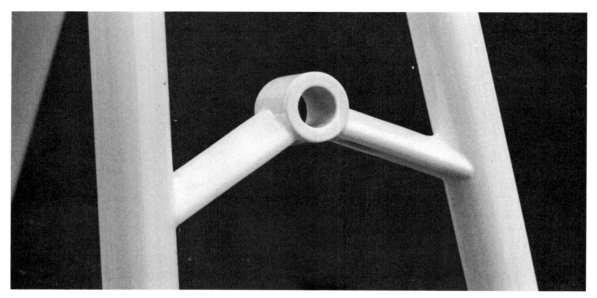

Fig 38   An aero section, investment cast, rear brake bridge.

Fig 39   Cinelli 509 top eyes; they have a large brazing contact area, ideal for heavy duty work.

key should be sufficient. Chapter 6 on Components details seat pillar sizes and problems.

For the seat-stay cluster forget shot-in stays: they are just about adequate for a time-trial bike but not for rigorous touring. Top eyes or top plates, with the seat stays fitting the side of the seat lug give the most practical arrangement. Cinelli make some short, very neat top eyes (*ref*: 509) that are machined to fit the side of the seat lug. The surface area of brazed contact is high, making a particularly strong joint. They are well suited to larger frames as the seat stays follow a closer line at the seat cluster – as though semi-shot in. If the seat stays are close at the seat lug then they are closer together at the brake bridge. The spacing of the seat stays at this point will determine the distance the cantilever bosses will be apart, which in turn affects their performance. As you can see, the design of seat cluster can affect seat-stay width at the brake fittings, so it is definitely worth considering.

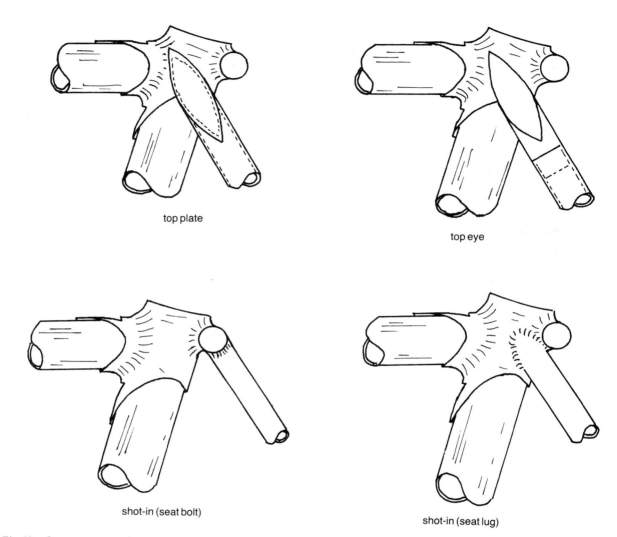

top plate

top eye

shot-in (seat bolt)

shot-in (seat lug)

Fig 40   Seat stay to seat lug arrangements. For touring forget shot-in stays as the area of brazing contact is relatively small.

Braze-on fittings are recommended. Most fittings are silver-brazed, and as a consequence, detriment to the tubing is negligible. Cantilever bosses are usually brass brazed but they are on heavy-gauge tubes and again the effects are negligible. Clamps around the tubes cause paint to chip and rust to set in, which in the long term will be much worse than the minute loss of strength caused by brazing on a boss.

I do not intend to go through each braze-on in turn as I believe the case for braze-ons has already been made. So, now you only need to decide which you require for your own frame – I shall suggest a few ideas but apart from that, the choice is yours.

Fig 41   *An unusual braze-on fitting, a bottle-cage boss in the brake bridge for direct attachment of the mudguard.*

Fig 42   *A simple route for the rear-brake cable with cantilevers forward of the seat stays – it is neat and functional.*

BRAKES

The rear brake cable normally goes on top of the top tube. This is easy for mass producers to do and it gets over the problem of side-pull brakes where one manufacturer has its arms on the left and another on the right.

My preference is based on personal comforts as I spend a lot of time chatting when on tour (usually waiting for a pub to open). I stand sideways to my bike and rest on the top tube. This is most uncomfortable with cable guides and a brake cable running along the top. Also, when I need to lift my bike and carry it, over a railway bridge for instance, I lift it so the side opposite to the oily chain set is on my right shoulder. Thus a brake cable running either underneath or down the left side of the frame gets in the way. I like my

brake cable to be on the lower right-hand side of the top tube, just sufficiently down its side so that when I look vertically down the frame the cable is just hidden under the vertical line of the tube.

I prefer and recommend two cable stops either end of the top tube. This minimises the amount of outer casing used in forming the rear brake cable run; outer casing compresses when the brake is applied which makes for a spongy feel. This is vital on tandems where long brake cable runs should always be free of outer casing.

On touring frames over about 22in, I often suggest placing the rear cantilever brake so it faces forward from the seat stays. The arms will be sufficiently out of the way of loaded pannier bags and it also ensures a particularly easy path for the rear brake cable. Fig 42 shows this set-up, with an outer-casing stop brazed off-centre on one of the seat stays. The off-centre nature of the straddle wire has no effect on the efficiency of the brakes but cannot be used on some models – such as Modolo cantilevers, as they have non-adjustable and individual straddle cables for each side. Care must be taken with small frames to make sure there is clearance between the heel and the cantilever arm. The principle of bag clearance is not quite as necessary with small frames as they enjoy laid-back seat stays so the pannier bags are further back from the brakes. It is large frames with steeper seat stays that require this feature so that they have the heel clearance.

Since the brake bosses are effectively facing downhill, they will fill with mud and water if the normally open face is not covered. As the pivots and brakes are facing downhill some cyclists wonder if the brakes might fall off. The answer is definitely no. The front brake is in effect running in a similar manner, the only difference being that the pivots face slightly uphill. They are both in effect trailing brakes and front brakes do not fall off, do they?

An alternative to cantilevers is braze-on centre-pulls. They are ideal for the cyclist who has weak hands and they do not foul pannier bags. It is not commonly known that braze-on pivots exist for these brakes, a design popular in both France and the USA. I have made some mention of their vices in Chapter 6 on Components, under Brakes.

Fig 43   Braze-on, centre-pull, Mafac 2000 brakes on the author's touring bike.

RACKS

Pannier racks are usually fitted to touring bikes. Four-point fitting to braze-on bosses is without doubt the best option for the rear, offering stability with heavy loads. Most pannier frames are designed to common dimensions, 13½in from fork-end eye to the rack's top surface. This means there is no standard distance between fork-end eye and rack boss. The 13½in rule works effectively with adjustable arm racks, but for models such as the

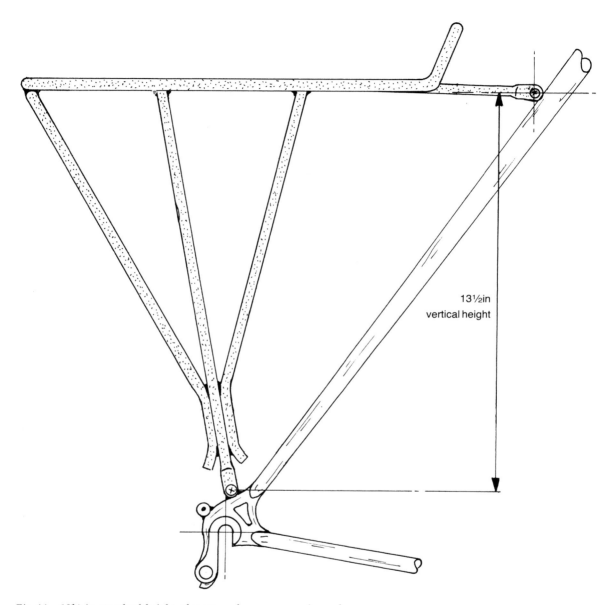

13½in
vertical height

Fig 44   13½ in standard height of most modern rear pannier racks.

Blackburn SS–1, SS–2 and SS–3 you may need to bend the arms a fraction to get the location correct and the rack horizontal. This is an item to discuss in depth with your frame builder.

Front racks are either low slung or a smaller version of a rear. Low-rider racks definitely feel better but, whichever you use, the front should only be used for light items such as sleeping bags. Jim Blackburn (the famous rack manufacturer from the States) makes a special low rack, the Custom Low-rider, which is neater than the standard version and is designed to be fitted to bosses brazed through the fork blade. I have brazed a few this way but only on thick blades such as 531 Super Tourist. Most other blades are thinner so I braze the bosses to the forward face of the fork blades.

Now I only use external bosses no matter what the type of fork blade as I have realised the positioning is far better. The carrier is designed for use with the lower mudguard eye of the fork-end. The carrier is also designed for typical American tourers (racing bikes with mudguard eyes and head angles of around 73 degrees). By fitting the boss forward using the upper eye of a twin eye fork-end, and with typical UK steering geometry, the rack is again sitting horizontal – all in all a far more satisfactory set-up.

Fig 45   Rear rack, braze-on bosses. An off-centre, cantilever straddle cable can also be seen. The direction of pull does not affect its efficiency.

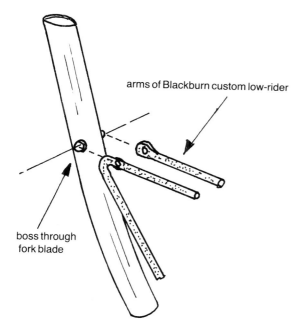

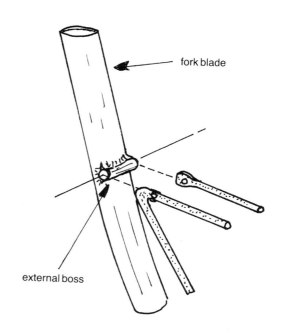

Fig 46   Jim Blackburn custom low-rider external fork bosses. These do not require the fork blade to be drilled and therefore do not weaken the fork, but look less neat.

Fig 47   A Jim Blackburn, custom, low-rider carrier. Much neater than the clamp-on model and I like a radially spoked front wheel, even on an ATB-size wheel.

FRAME FINISH

Colour and paint finish is a personal choice where the customer is always right (however evil I think it might be). It is a good job we are all different; however, I do point out a few little facts regarding the use of stove-enamel paints rather than multi-pacs or epoxy versions, which are popular in the States where stoving ovens do not traditionally exist.

Basic enamel is the hardest wearing, closely followed by metallics. Polychromatics seem very thin and flamboyants (flams) are the most difficult to touch up. Flams do not wear too badly, they look super when new with their high-gloss sheen, but once scratched it is another matter. The process involves a layer of reflective-type paint, a layer of colour dye and then layers of lacquer – you cannot get that in a bottle or paint-stick.

Enamels are best touched up with model paints available in better toy shops. Airfix or Humbrol should do and if the colour does not exactly match you will have to sit down and laboriously mix a few tins until it does. Touch-up paint from the sprayer is usually no good as it is designed for spray application and has the consistency of water; it will not fill chips.

Metallic paints are not like car metallics which have a dire reputation. Stoving metallics are tough and recommended. Touch-up from the paint shop is usually much thicker and works well on chips. Touching up polychromatics and flamboyants can only be second-rate and done with enamels, which will never look quite right.

Fluorescent paints are now the vogue. I think they are totally tasteless but then I have never been a 'trendy' person. They spray to a matt finish and usually get sparkled up by several top coats of gloss lacquer. Time will tell as to their durability.

Chrome is debated and argued about at great length. As far as I am concerned there is no debate; I simply forbid any on my frames. I allowed chrome on a few frames a long time ago but I soon learned my lesson and now I simply refuse. Chrome is forbidden by Reynolds on their 753 as it causes hydrogen embrittlement, a technical term for 'it will eventually break'. Columbus make recommendations in their catalogue stating that they do not recommend the use of chrome on

Fig 48   Vertical drop-outs on a well-used bike. The wheel entry is clean so paint does not appear to have been scraped off, so no need for chrome.

their products but, if you must have it, a certain procedure should be followed. (It is strange that most Italian frames are covered with chrome!)

The chroming process physically and chemically does all sorts of nasty things to your frame. Firstly, considerable amounts of metal are stripped from the parts to be chromed at the polishers. The metal surfaces must be totally free from blemishes, so what are already thin tubes may be made even thinner. After polishing, the tubes are dunked in acids, neutralising baths and all sorts of corrosive brews – not the way to treat a precision work of art. Problems continue at the paint shop, trying to get the paint to stick to the chrome at the interfaces. The chrome does not magically stop just where the paint starts. There is an overlap so there is paint on top of the chrome, but paint requires a rough surface to key it to any metal. Chrome is so hard that grit at the blasting shop makes negligible impression and so the undercoat has to stick to a highly smooth surface. Inevitably the paint peels off in no time. The enameller tries hard by using special acidic primers to assist grip but the job can be nothing but second-rate.

Eventually the chrome rusts. Modern chroming techniques, although conforming to quoted standards, do not include the copper and nickel layers found on older frames. Copper forms a non-porous barrier stopping moisture reaching the steel whereas chrome, being porous, allows the steel/water reaction to occur – rusting. The problem now is to remove the rusty mess before it can be resprayed or, if you have not learned your lesson, rechromed. There are reverse chemical/electrical methods of removal but usually a big, nasty-looking file is used. If the chrome is not totally removed it will continue to flake after painting, taking new paint with it.

I know chrome looks nice and I know fork-ends look less than attractive with the paint scraped off. However, I advise an adjustment of mind; learn to loathe the look of chrome and accept these minor problems. I now use vertical fork-ends, which do not have the long redundant slots of road fork-ends. Consequently, the only area scraped free of paint by the wheel nuts is the area under the nut (which is invisible). Stick-on chrome-looking plastic chain stay protectors are very efficient at protecting the right-hand chain stay from a flailing chain. So why use chrome?

3 Specialised Frames

SMALL FRAMES

Custom frame builders design and build a high percentage of little frames. Mass producers ignore and seem not even to understand the subtleties of making small frames. The compromises to be considered require a totally different approach as there is a lot more to a small bike than just a shorter seat tube.

Areas of ignorance include the bottom bracket height, crank length and top tube length. To start, I will analyse the problems common to the short-legged cyclist. The first observation of small frames with 27in wheels, be they 27 × 1¼in or 700c, is that the bottom bracket height is too high. A 20in frame for such wheels with a bottom bracket height of 10½in will have a very short head tube, so short that the top and down tubes touch each other.

To produce a frame smaller than 20in,

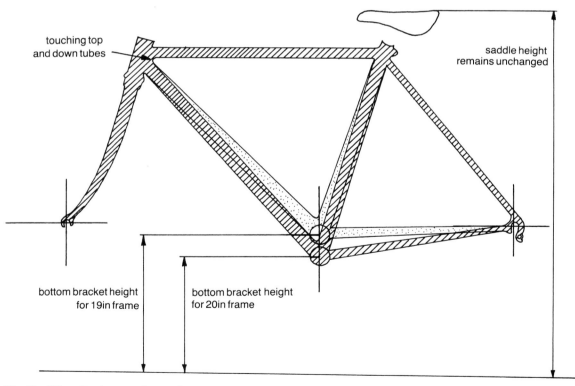

Fig 49   When the down and top tubes meet at the head cluster, the only way to make a smaller frame (dotted) is to raise the bottom-bracket height.

the bottom bracket height must be raised above 10½in as the head tube cannot be any shorter. So a 19in frame will have a 11½in bottom bracket height. This seems to be nonsense as the top tube will be as far away from the ground on both the 19in and 20in frames, but believe me this is what happens. The practical implication is that short-legged cyclists cannot reach the ground when they stop. Quite simply, short legs cannot articulate over the same extremes; for the same reason short legs need short cranks to stop unnecessary fatigue.

The bracket height should be calculated from the pedal clearance required for your style of riding and the crank length suited to your leg length. It is amazing how many 19in-frame riders use 170mm cranks, often in ignorance but often as other lengths are more expensive. I cannot overemphasise the need for thought in this area, particularly when designing a new custom frame. Assuming you have got short cranks to make your pedal action more efficient, you can now have a lower bottom bracket on your frame. When you stop it will now be possible to

Fig 50   An 18½in touring bike with 26in ATB wheels. It all looks and behaves in good proportion.

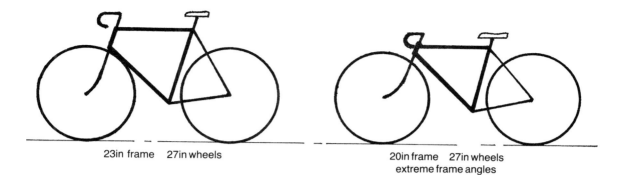

23in frame   27in wheels

20in frame   27in wheels
extreme frame angles

19in frame   27in wheels
standard angles (impossible combination)

18in frame   ATB wheels
standard angles

19in frame   650b wheels
angles close to standard

19in frame   ATB wheels
standard angles and low BB

Fig 51   Comparisons of small frames with 27in, 26in (650b) and 26in (ATB) wheels. Smaller wheels create a bike of better balance. There are many permutations, here are some ideas.

place your feet, or at least one foot, firmly on the ground.

The custom builder can approach the lower bottom bracket in a number of ways. If 27in wheels are a must, the only way to build the frame is with a sloping top tube, sloping downhill from the head tube to the seat tube. I believe a better option is to use smaller wheels, usually 26in in either the UK format of 26 × 1¼in or the French equivalent of 650b. You could opt for the ATB size of 26 × 1½in, especially today since narrower rims and road tyres are readily available.

The choice of smaller wheels also solves the other main problem of small frames – top tubes which are too long. Assuming short legs are matched with a short body, then a short top tube is necessary but this often conflicts with the requirement that the pedal and toe-clip, assuming it is fitted, does not foul the front wheel and mudguard. With normal frame geometry a short top tube will give a lot of pedal overlap. The only way to minimise or eliminate this overlap is to consider all or some of the following methods: use smaller wheels, short cranks, small toe-clips, or go to extreme frame angles.

I find it odd that the last method is usually accepted as the norm. I have often heard that small frames necessitate very shallow head angles and super steep seat angles, to fit the smaller body. This is utter rubbish. It is the ratio of body parts that determines angles and not overall size. A normally proportioned six-foot rider has his knee, say, 50 per cent of the way down his leg. A normally proportioned four-foot eight-inch rider also has his knee 50 per cent of the way down his leg, although the lengths are obviously very different. It is the ratio of upper to lower leg length that determines the seat angle. Both riders will need the same seat angle, probably 73 degrees.

Most small cyclists need an identical angled design to an average-size person, the smaller frame will just be a scaled-down version. The common approach for a 19in touring frame with 27in wheels typically gives a 70 degree head angle, 76 degree seat angle, 11½in bottom bracket height and toe-clips that still hit the front mudguard. The small wheel approach gives a 72 degree head angle, 73 degree seat angle, 10¼in bracket height and no overlap of clip and guard. The advantage of the latter is that it will handle and respond better simply because it is not so compromised.

There are practical problems to consider in building small frames. If you opt for extreme frame angles quality lugs will be difficult to find or it becomes necessary to bend standard lugs to meet these extremes. With the small wheel design the top head lug and seat lug are normal and so there is no problem. The lower head lug needs to be shallow angled and the builder may have to search far to find such a lug. The bottom-bracket shell must be differently angled to the standard, the angle between down tube and seat tube being very small; suitable cast bottom bracket shells may be hard to find, but they are made, usually Japanese in origin (since the Japanese are in general a nation of shorter people).

Another concern of builders is the position of the butting within the tubes, particularly the down and top tubes. Reynolds (as a typical example) supply butted frame tubes in one length, the thin central butt accurately positioned off-centre towards one end. The builder first machines the end with the short butt and then removes excess material from the other end to produce a tube of the required length. However, when the tubes have to be very short, as in an 18in frame, the tube may become so short that no butt

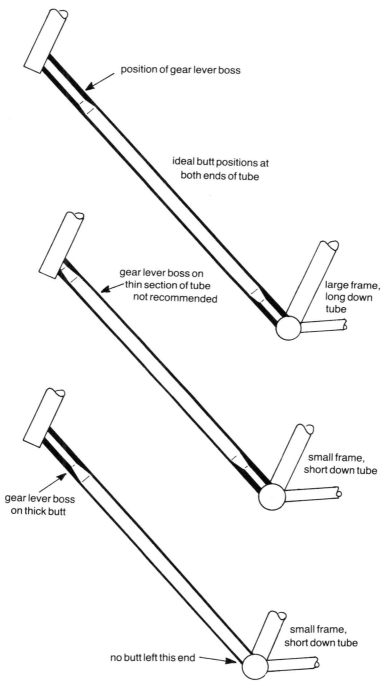

position of gear lever boss

ideal butt positions at
both ends of tube

gear lever boss on
thin section of tube
not recommended

large frame,
long down
tube

small frame,
short down tube

gear lever boss
on thick butt

small frame,
short down tube

no butt left this end

*Fig 52   Small-frame down tubes: the thin butt may be too long and extend
into the head lug or bottom-bracket shell. The gear lever boss should also be on
a thick butt. Careful selection of tube can overcome this problem.*

59

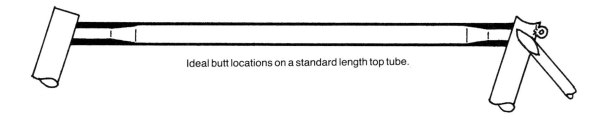

Ideal butt locations on a standard length top tube.

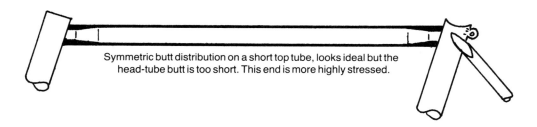

Symmetric butt distribution on a short top tube, looks ideal but the head-tube butt is too short. This end is more highly stressed.

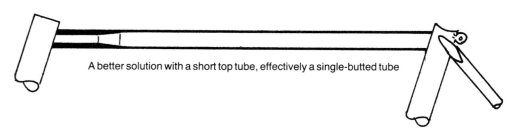

A better solution with a short top tube, effectively a single-butted tube

Fig 53   Short top tubes are better with no butt at seat lug end than a short butt at head tube end.

remains at one of its ends. In effect the tube becomes single-butted. This is fine for the top tube, as long as the thick butt is at the head-tube end, but not for the down tube. If the central thin butt comes too close or actually goes through to either the head tube or the bottom-bracket shell premature fatigue failure will occur. The answer is to use a heavier gauge tube, to use a plain gauge tube, or to consider specially manufactured butted tubes made for small frames.

The last option is available from Columbus who offer most of their frame tube sets in three sizes, for large, medium and small frames. I often use a Columbus, small-size down tube in 19in frames, even those built from Reynolds 531 tubing. This argument is particularly valid with light frames (frames made from thin gauge tubing). In addition to the problem of the thin butt exiting the tube end, it is

Fig 54   Fatigue crack from a Campagnolo lever boss on very thin tubing, Reynolds 531Pro.

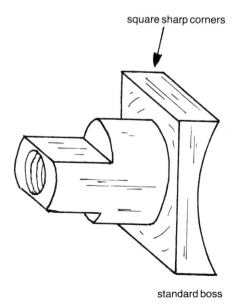

square sharp corners

standard boss

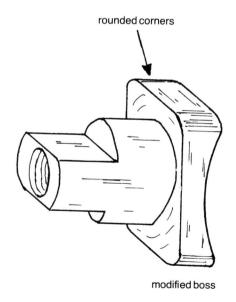

rounded corners

modified boss

Fig 55   The standard Campagnolo gear lever boss and one with rounded shoulders to minimise stress raisers.

61

important to try and position braze-on gear lever bosses on the thick-butted section of the down tube. Campagnolo gear lever bosses are quite nasty when it comes to stress raisers; they have four sharp corners that propagate fatigue cracks, breaking the down tube with remarkable efficiency.

I mentioned earlier that it is okay to have a single-butted top tube. In fact, I often build this way on purpose, especially on frames with oversize top tubes. The back-end of the top tube is lightly stressed and like the seat tube will survive without butted reinforcement. It is a way of having a considerably stiffer oversize top tube that is no heavier than a normal top tube.

LARGE FRAMES

Large frames do not create the same problems as small ones but none the less they still need some special consideration. There are fortunately no heart-searching decisions to be made over conflicting interests of practicality. For similar reasons of scarceness, the custom builder creates as high a percentage of large frames as he does small. Mass produced frames are usually 25in maximum; so if you need larger then there is often no option but to consider custom built.

Large frames are usually long in the top tube, resulting in long wheelbases if standard frame angles are kept. One way to maintain a long top tube and shorten the wheelbase to the normal size is to incorporate a steep head angle and a shallow seat angle – do not fall for this. Large and therefore tall frames need longer wheelbases in order to offer comparable stability and handling characteristics to smaller frames; after all they have a higher centre of gravity to put up with.

As with small frames there are some problems of practicality that the builder must address. Bottom head lugs and bottom-bracket shells with large angles, necessary with big frames, are rare so choice may be limited. Columbus tubes, from their long set, make into frames up to 26in and Reynolds make a giant set in heavy gauge, for frames up to 30in. The combination of longer tubes and the fact that tall riders are generally heavier, can lead to handling difficulties when in camping/cycle touring bikes. Several approaches have been made to reinforce large frames to try to make them stiffer for more arduous work: double top tubes; additional twin lateral tubes as on women's frames; full-size lateral bracing tubes as on better tandems; and oversize main tubes have all been used to various degrees of success.

An oversize top tube is the simplest start, i.e. the use of a down tube as a top tube. With the advent of ATBs, oversize down tubes are now a serious consideration, especially since they now come in various grades of plain gauge, double-, triple- and quadruple-butting. Sadly only a few are long enough for the job. These new tubes offer the most elegant way to produce a large, very stiff frame. Double top tubes of standard diameter only benefit the top part of the frame (the area least stressed) and they look terrible. A similar argument follows for oversize top tubes, except that this option looks more normal. The least desirable of all the options is the use of women's style twin lateral tubes from the head tube to the rear fork-ends. As you will read at great length in the Tandem and Women's Frame sections, twin lateral tubes should be restricted to shopping bikes. They offer no lateral rigidity, especially along the axis of their position, which coincides with the main axis along which the frame twists!

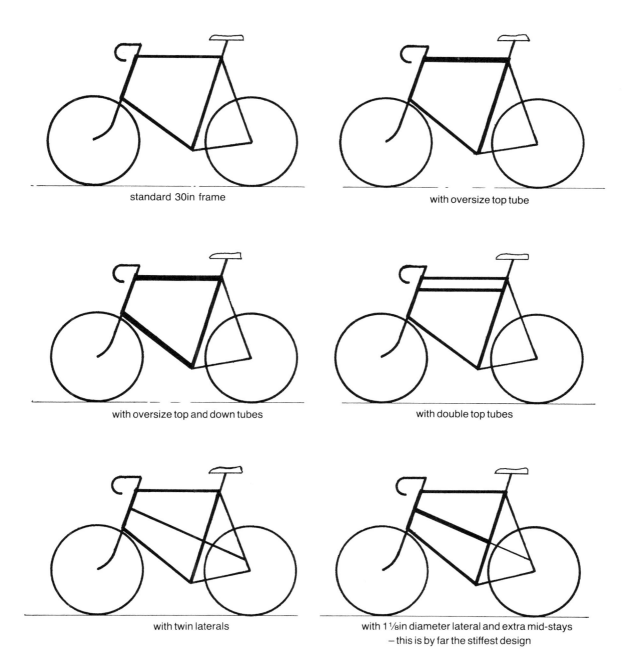

standard 30in frame

with oversize top tube

with oversize top and down tubes

with double top tubes

with twin laterals

with 1⅛in diameter lateral and extra mid-stays
– this is by far the stiffest design

Fig 56   Large frames (possible reinforcing arrangements).

63

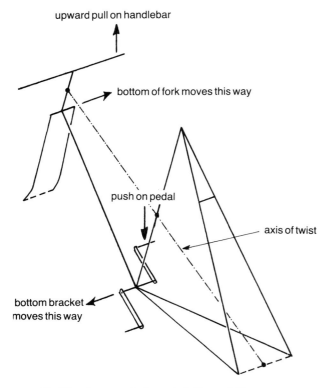

upward pull on handlebar

bottom of fork moves this way

push on pedal

axis of twist

bottom bracket
moves this way

Fig 57   A women's frame twisting uphill.

Since this line between head tube and rear fork-ends is the twist axis, placing a torque resistant structure in this line can be of benefit. A full size or oversize tube, with additional stays within the rear triangle, is very effective at controlling twist. However, this option is the most expensive as the work content is high. My recommendation, if, and only if, standard tubes are inadequate, is to forget extra tubes and go for the value for money option of oversize down and top tubes. Lugs for these oversize tubes in non-ATB angles do not exist, so lugless or semi-lugged construction must be used, or even a combination of lugless and semi-lugged.

For practical reasons, I prefer to use an oversize head tube (33mm) with lugless

joints and a semi-lugged seat cluster. These arguments are expanded in the lugless construction section in Chapter 1.

WOMEN'S FRAMES

Picture this scenario: a 1-in-5 hill (going up of course), Welsh rain, a head wind, and it is supposedly a dry country. In this situation, I bet you ask yourself the same question I ponder over: 'Why do women ride frames where primary structural bracing members exhibit negligible resistance to cyclically applied torque?' After all, there is little else to occupy your mind in such misery, and hills are hard enough with a properly designed structure – the men's frame.

There are efficient designs for women but they are rare. The majority of these designs are a disaster, suffering chronic lateral flexure, which absorbs effort in winding the frame up and not projecting forward. I accept that some ladies will not ride a man's frame but I do try to persuade otherwise. If I fail to convince, I am forced to explain how to design a good women's frame – which goes basically as follows.

Initially, one must analyse how a frame bends when pedalling under stress, (uphill, for instance). When you push on the right-hand pedal you automatically compensate by pulling on the right-hand handlebar. The result is a twisting action through the frame, closely following a line from the head tube to the rear drop-outs. The typical women's frame designs, especially in the quality market, have twin lateral tubes which precisely follow this line of twist. For the frame to be efficient, the lateral bracing must discourage twist and sadly twin laterals do not.

As I hope you can see from Figs 57 and 58, twin lateral tubes do little to resist twist. They are quite efficient in control-

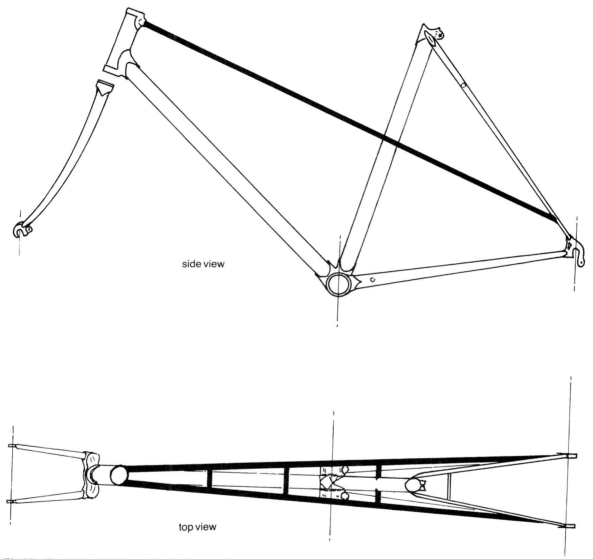

side view

top view

*Fig 58   Twin lateral tubes – they look pretty but do nothing for lateral
torque.*

ling bending forces, but only in one plane
– a plane of small consequence to frame
twist. Twin lats (as they are affectionately
or, in my case, unaffectionately known)
may look the part and their dainty nature
finds favour with many fashion-
conscious women; they are ideal for the

casual shopper but not, in my opinion, for
serious cyclists.

We must therefore discuss alternatives.
There are alternatives which strangely
enough can be found on cheaper bikes
sold as down-market versions. They have
a full-size top tube following a line identi-

Fig 59   A simple but effective women's design; better than twin lats!

cal to twin lats from the top of the head tube to a point about three-quarters of the way up the seat tube. Better versions from the more informed frame builders have an oversize (1⅛in diameter) top tube with additional stays from the top tube/seat tube intersection back to the rear fork-ends, as in twin lats. These extra rear stays (mid-stays) stiffen the rear half of the frame as well as supporting the seat tube, which in the woman's version suffers bending forces not present in a man's design.

Bending comes simply by sitting on the saddle and thereafter every time the bike suffers vertical depositions, bumps and pot-holes and so on. The wheels ultimately transmit loadings from frame to the road surface and as the frame is loaded the bottom bracket will slightly fall. To resist this action stresses are transmitted along the top tube and seat stays causing a bending couple within the seat tube. Extra mid-stays will support the seat tube at this point to eliminate these bendings. Alternatively, or additionally, a thicker gauge seat tube can be used.

Reynolds appreciated this dilemma and, in 1989, introduced a special seat tube. The single butt at the lower end of the tube is 280mm, long enough to reach the point where the lateral tubes cross. So the best women's frames have a 1⅛in top tube with additional mid-stays, both following a straight line from the top of the head tube to the rear drop-outs.

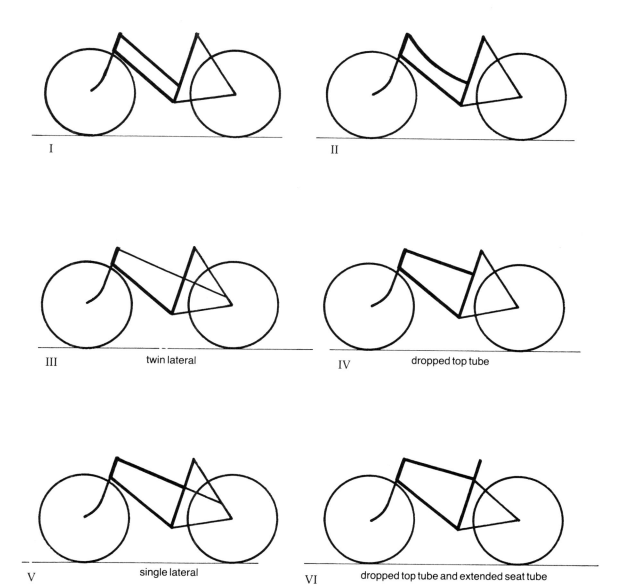

Fig 60 Options for women's frames when a conventional top tube is out of the question. I and II are for pretend bikes; III is popular but of dubious merit; IV is much better; V is the stiffest; VI is a worthy compromise between IV and V.

Fig 61   A design for serious touring. The extra tubes and complicated methods of construction make it a little expensive.

This design is in fact rather good and if carefully executed can produce a frame better than a men's frame. The argument is of course subjective and although I believe it to be valid for small frames, 19–21in, it may not be strictly true for 23in or larger. One thing you can definitely say is that the women's frame will be heavier than the men's equivalent as thicker, larger and additional tubes all add up. Unfortunately, they also add up on the cash register, not because two extra tubes cost much, but the methods of construction are complex and time costs money.

All other aspects of the frame geometry and sizing follow identical arguments to those presented in Chapter 1. The only

exception is the position and type of rear brake. The standard rear brake fitting, on the seat-stay bridge, creates an awkward cable run, having to double-bend from the top tube to the seat stays. Many side-pull brake manufacturers offer a women's version where the cable approaches the brake from below and is fastened with an anchor bolt on the upper arm (upside down to the standard).

The main problem arises with centre-pull and cantilever brakes. The cable must come down from the seat lug cluster at the top of the seat tube. Termination of the outer casing must be high up the seat stays and the resulting cable run is tortuous, leading to long-term problems of sticking cables. One elegant solution is to arrange the brake to be positioned on the mid-stays. I favour the use of centre-pulls for this positioning but I have known both side-pulls and cantilevers to work satisfactorily. However, take care with both these latter options. Cantilever arms and the arms of side-pulls can stick out and foul your feet, depending on their exact position, your foot size and your pedalling style. Some cyclists pedal with their toes out, their heels pointing in.

Centre-pulls do not protrude outside the limits of the stays and they are particularly good brakes for women since their mechanical advantages, or mechanical characteristics, are well suited to weaker hands. The most elegant solution is to fit centre-pulls with braze-on pivots, as

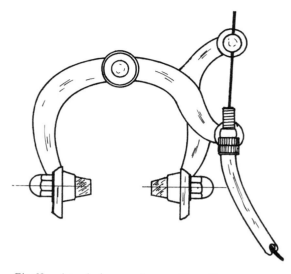

Fig 62   A typical women's rear side-pull brake where the cable enters from below.

Fig 63   Braze-on, Mafac Racer, centre-pull brakes on the mid stays of a women's frame (note the efficient cable run). A good brake set-up.

offered by Mafac or Dia-Compe. These braze-on versions have just been re-invented by the ATB fraternity. They call them 'U brakes', but many tourists have known of their excellence for years. With a centre-pull stirrup in this position, the straddle wire has to be replaced by a longer version and positioned so that the cable clamp/straddle puller is positioned in front of the seat tube. The cable run to such a brake is short and totally straight, so concluding a very efficient set-up.

The braze-on pivots eliminate most of the spongy feel associated with centre-pull brakes. I find this set-up so good I incorporate it into many tandems, as the prime rear brake! It is unorthodox and as such meets resistance but converts are on the increase.

Well that is it, ladies, except I cannot close without passing some comment based on observations I have made over the years. Many couples find their speed and abilities different, often solved by a tandem but often not. It puzzles me that in many cases he has a super all-singing frame set with components to match, while she has cast-offs, cheaper tubing and a rotten design. No wonder riding capabilities appear different. Gents, if your companion is of a weaker disposition then she needs all the help she can get – you ride the junk and get her on to 753.

4 All-terrain Bikes (ATBs)

It must be difficult to write a book about ATBs – the fads change so fast, how can one keep up to date? I love off-road riding and the ATB has brought a new meaning to my rough-stuff as I no longer need to worry about wheel collapse or losing grip. For the wanderer and lover of wild country they are brilliant. However, a lot of traditional cyclists are put off by their reputation for horrendous weight. Most ATBs are heavy; they need to be as cyclists expect to treat them with total disregard and to ride them in all conditions. Yet strong and light frames can be built and many such beasts have been created by several custom builders. The question is, do we have an ATB or a touring bike that utilises mountain-bike wheels?

Fig 64   State-of-the-art Dave Yates ATB. (Photo by Mike Craig)

Fig 65   The author's touring ATB on a small hill in Arctic Norway!

I build very few traditional-style mountain bike frames; after all, with so much built-in overkill it does not require skill to build a tough bike. In fact it is not always good value for money to buy a custom ATB frame, of traditional style, from a custom frame builder. If we are honest, most of the mass-produced frames are equally adequate. Either robot or craftsman can build a tank but only a craftsman can build your dream machine. (Yes, you are right, I think most mountain bikes are tanks.)

Since this book is about touring bikes I shall ignore details of ATB novelties, the slalom frames and hill-climb specials. I believe ATBs offer a lot for touring and this is what I wish to concentrate on.

You do not need thick, heavy, oversize tank tubes for an off-road bike. Standard touring tube sets, Reynolds 531ST or Columbus SP/SPX are ideal. For years, cyclists have been doing rough-stuff on standard bicycles without frame breakages. But then these cyclists have different riding techniques, ones that looks after the bike more. I have been cross-country riding with mixed groups, some on ATBs and some not. Speeds and abilities are very similar, the only real advantage of the ATB being the fat tyre. The advantage for the touring-bike riders is that they do not have hernias when crossing styles, gates and rock faces.

Most of my ATB orders are for light, touring versions. I sometimes use over-

Fig 66   Cycle-camping in Lapland, ideal mountain bike country,
photographed here on a two-plank wooden bridge.

size tubing but not normally. If fat tyres, 2⅛in type, are required I have to use ATB-style chain stays and fork crowns or unicrowns. These chain stays are heavy, especially those from Reynolds. I normally use Columbus since they are sensibly thinner and lighter. Whilst I and a few other touring-biased builders consider lighter tube sets of benefit in the ATB/touring guise, the ATB market is demanding heavier and larger tubes. The 1990 Reynolds ATB range includes the traditional oversize tubes in 501, 531, 653 and 753, but in addition there is a 'mega-size' tube set called the Magnum 531. It has a 34mm triple-butted down tube and,

in the future, Reynolds are to market lugs and a bottom-bracket shell to complement these huge tank tubes. I marvel at the extremes to which fashion has driven this market.

If narrow ATB tyres are all that is required, standard 531ST chain stays are adequate. I give them a little bend to allow a touch more clearance but the angle is marginal. Touring forks are strong enough but the final choice again depends on tyre choice. My all-terrain bike is made from 753 tubing with a maximum width clearance for 1.9in tyres. It weighs 22lb and can easily be carried on a rucksack. It has survived a six-week off-

*Fig 67   An extended head tube allows a
normal height top tube with a high bottom
bracket.*

road expedition across Lapland, laden
with a hundredweight of survival gear,
and over some of the most appalling rock
fields imaginable. I do not necessarily
recommend 753; it is easy for me as
a frame builder to knock up my own
specials, but I do recommend the design
and philosophy of lightness, especially
for touring.

A typical touring ATB bike works out
with a 71-degree head angle, 73-degree
seat angle, 11in bottom-bracket height,
17¾in chain stays and a 2⅛in fork offset.
Variations are of course made for indi-
viduals. The resulting bike is light, nimble
and practical, with good handling. Components are again to choice but I have
successfully used very wide drop handlebars, the extra width offering better control on the rough and the drops more
options on the road. I know brake levers
feel better with straight bars and I would
use straight bars for true off-road riding,
but on a dual purpose bike the wide drop
bar is a compromise worth consideration.

For the international tourist, the 26in
ATB wheel size is about the most universally available. As many cyclists know,
getting 700c tyres in Ireland or 27in tyres
in France can be a problem, not so with
the 26in ATB sizing. If you tour wild
country, give the ATB tyre some thought
– they are not all heavy or slow riding.

5 Tandems, Triplets and Trikes

TANDEMS

They say you only have memories when you are old. Perhaps so, and perhaps I am a bit, but there is nothing quite so memorable as riding on the back of a tandem. In the early seventies I attempted some racing – tandem racing. Being wiry, light and reasonably strong my physique suggested I stoked, the stoker being the person on the back (the one kids on the street laugh at). I am basically bone idle or perhaps I cannot quite see the point of racing, but whatever the reason I get bored riding a time trial as my interest wanders. Having to look where I am going distracts me from the mental effort it takes for me to pedal hard. But on the back of the tandem it is totally different. You shut your eyes, wring hell out of the handlebars and do nothing but concentrate on one thing – going fast. The pain comes and goes but so what, it is great and if I did not give it my all I would be letting my partner down. I remember the lack of wind noise, as the horrible mass of sweating athletes in front provides good shelter. Then I remember the hum of 120psi tubular tyre skimming the road surface. The noise is phenomenal. Then I remember the seasickness, the oddest of sensations cornering a fast roundabout in a trance. You have no idea of its presence until the tandem leans left, then right, then left again. Stoking is brilliant.

When touring I tend to go on the front, except after a good dinner-time session when Christine may decide she had better take charge. We are both close in size and can swap positions simply by moving the seat pillars a little. The advantages of a tandem are well understood. Togetherness, particularly for two cyclists of different ability. Conversations are easy to maintain and in general tandems are quicker. However, they do not suit everyone. For this reason I recommend that you try tandem riding before spending vast amounts of money on a custom job. If you can borrow a tandem, hire a tandem or buy a cheap tandem, do so for a period of at least a couple of months. You must accept it may have mechanical shortcomings; you are merely testing each other's attitude towards tandem riding, not the machine. Many couples just cannot get on riding together all the time.

A common problem with many tandems is comfort – the lack of it. Sore backsides are the main complaint; there are two reasons for this, both particular to tandems. The first is bump reactions. When the front wheel hits a bump the front of the tandem is raised. This lifts the captain, both his handlebars and saddle at the same time. The rear wheel similarly hitting the bump will raise all of the stoker in one go. A solo bicycle, however, seesaws the rider, the front wheel lifting only the handlebars and the rear wheel only the saddle. The second reason is that it is harder for both riders on a tandem to move about and perform normal habits such as lifting your backside just slightly

Fig 68 Tandeming, actually tandem triking, in mid-Wales.

off the saddle. The stoker suffers more so from this as the riding position is usually more cramped and he cannot see when bumps approach.

If you are committed to the idea of a good tandem, I am afraid it will not be cheap. Most tandems use solo bicycle components and with both the weight and power of two to contend with, equipment gets quite a pounding. This means cheap wheels, brakes, blocks, head sets and chain sets do not last. It pays in the long term to invest in quality, not only due to the cost of always having to replace cheap, broken parts but because breakdowns of specialist tandem parts in remote areas cannot be solved by local hardware shops. However, do not go berserk on things like gear mechanisms, handlebars, mudguards and other non-stressed items; as with a solo, select value-for-money components.

The frame is the heart of the tandem and frames in the last ten years have improved dramatically. New materials are available and new and more efficient designs make your choice difficult but a lot more interesting. The buoyant ATB market has helped, as many parts are compatible with tandems, including frame tubes. On the design front we now see much longer rear top tubes, an improvement for the stoker position but necessitating frame bracing to be re-examined. Consequently complex designs, such as the double marathon, are in demand.

In designing the frame there are many compromises to consider. Cost is often a dominant factor but I shall ignore money in these arguments since this subject should be reserved for the customer and perhaps his bank manager. Prices of tandem frames vary much more than solos, reflecting the multitude of construction techniques available and adopted. The

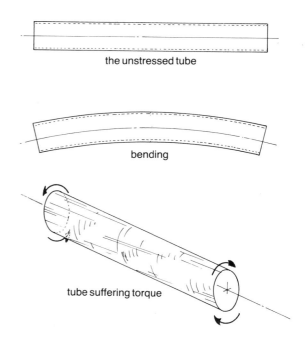

Fig 69   Bending and twisting (torque) of a simple tube.

cheapest options are solo diameter tubes and lugs – 1in diameter top tubes and 1⅛in diameter down tubes. There are other options for the more adventurous frame builder, who may consider oversize top, down, head and even seat tubes, together with larger chain stays, seat stays and fork blades. These larger tubes do not themselves incur much of a cost penalty but they necessitate complex techniques of building which put the cost up. I will only use oversize main tubes as I am convinced they are essential for a quality frame set.

The stiffness of a tube, to both torque and bending, is a function of its diameter to the power of four. So if you double the tube diameter you increase the stiffness by a factor of sixteen. However, doubling the diameter would make the frame unbearably heavy so you have to compromise. If you double the diameter but make the tube thinner, it weighs the same. The resulting tube is theoretically stiffer but the walls are so thin they will crumple, just like an empty cola can.

There is an optimum compromise between weight, tube wall thickness and tube diameter. It is no coincidence that solo bikes, built in steel, have 1in top tubes and 1⅛in down and seat tubes. Their diameters have been experimented with for decades and the conclusions are still valid. Tandem needs have been neglected in recent years. Old tandems, pre-War and those just post-War usually had oversize frame tubes. The sixties brought compromises and solo diameter tandem tubes came into favour. Applying the same logic to the compromise equation for tandem frames, the optimum diameters for the tubes are 1⅛in for seat, top and lateral bracing tubes, and 1¼in for down tube. Expedition tandems

can benefit from 1⅜in down tubes but generally speaking these are a bit excessive.

The design of internal bracing tubes can have a bearing on main-frame diameter choice. An unbraced frame can survive if it has the largest frame tubes practicable, such as a 1⅜in down tube. A well-braced structure, such as the double marathon, will perform to an optimum with 1¼in and 1⅛in diameter tubes.

Tandem tube sets are marketed by both Reynolds and Columbus. Ishiwata have attempted to infiltrate the UK scene but their tandem set was never popular (probably because of the coals to Newcastle syndrome). Reynolds market two sets in 531, one with solo size tubes and round drainpipe and the other, more for custom frames, with oversize tubes and oval drainpipe. A 753 set is also available but sadly it comprises solo diameter tubes. It

Fig 70 Double marathon design tandem (looks like a five-bar gate but goes like the wind).

has not been received with much enthusiasm but I can understand Reynolds' thoughts.

The only lug sets available (and lugs are deemed desirable with 753) are for solo diameter tubes. It is possible to lugless silver-braze oversize 753 but it requires a great deal of patience and it is also expensive. I have built a few lugless 753 tandems and I actually ride one. The tubes are oversize, mainly 753R down tubes, resulting in an amazingly nimble and responsive double marathon, weighing only 30lb complete with eighteen gears, lights and carrier.

Columbus market two sets, the Tandem CR in chrome molybdenum tubing with solo diameter tubes and round drainpipe, and the Tandem CM in superior chrome molybdenum Cyclex steel, using oversize tubes, a giant 35mm plain gauge down tube, an oval drainpipe and colossal 35mm × 22mm fork blades and chain stays. The seat and top tubes are pinched from the SPX range and incorporate helical reinforcing ribs on the internal thick butts – a truly magnificent tube specification brought about by Santana Cycles in the USA (a company devoted to quality tandems). The problem in the UK is to find a fork crown to fit the enormous blades. The oval chain stays are rather unnecessary, their oval section being stiffer in exactly the wrong plane – vertically. Their giant size looks the part, but in reality their section cannot withstand the all-important lateral stresses that cause back-ends to flex. A simple round 22mm chain stay of equivalent gauge is not only adequate, it is better.

For the true custom builder, sets are not important. Reynolds tubing is fortunately marketed so that individual tubes are available. I select each tube from their vast range to build a true one-off. Most Columbus tubes are available individually so

my designs benefit from a mix of Reynolds and Columbus steels. To round off the international flavour, I now use 33mm oversize chrome molybdenum head tubes from Vitus of France. (*See* section on head tubes on pages 86–90.)

Design Options

Unbraced

Not worthy of consideration for serious use. It lacks lateral stiffness but is the cheapest to build. The heaviest tubes, in both gauge and diameter are necessary to compensate for design shortcomings, resulting in a rather heavy and dead tandem.

Double Diamond

Initially this design may look ideal; it is fairly cheap to build and very popular. It resembles a girder bridge and as such supports the rider's weight well. However, structural requirements are much more complex as the problem is how to construct a planer device – one in just two dimensions that can accommodate three-dimensional twisting and bending forces (actions caused by pedalling).

When you push the left pedal, you pull on the left handlebar – action and reaction. This causes a complex distribution of twist and bending throughout each tube but the general result is that the front bottom bracket flaps from side-to-side. The front bracket is supported mainly by the down tube and drainpipe, hence the advantage of their being large and stiff. The purpose of internal frame bracing on a tandem is to assist both of these highly stressed tubes. However, the rear cross tube of a double diamond fails since its position is remote from the front bracket.

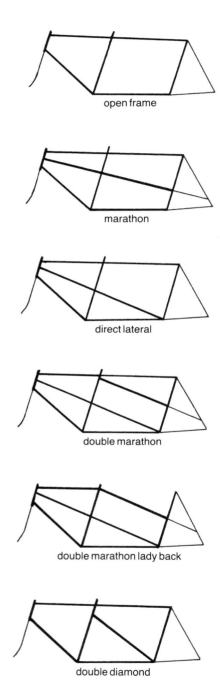

open frame

marathon

direct lateral

double marathon

double marathon lady back

double diamond

Fig 71 Common design options for tandem bracing.

Marathon

There is a lot going for this old design. The extra tube in the front helps to support the front bottom bracket and the lateral tubes, from head tube to rear fork-ends, and controls lateral twist admirably. The line of these lateral tubes happens to be that of the axis of the frame twist when pedalling hard. This is an excellent design for couples who have similar power outputs, because both front and rear halves are equally supported by the bracing tubes.

Direct Lateral

This relatively new design is gaining popularity. It is easier to build than a marathon so is favoured by manufacturers. It is a particularly good design for couples of uneven strengths. The lateral tubes cross the front seat tube lower than the marathon, thus supporting the front bottom bracket better. However, the rear half of the frame is not so well supported, hence my recommendation that it is ridden by a strong captain and a weaker stoker (if you are of similar strengths, go for a marathon or double marathon). The direct lateral also finds favour with couples who are of vastly different sizes. The reason for this is that the larger captain needs more support at his end of the frame. Direct laterals are now very popular and in many cases they deserve to be, but do not forget the difficulties they present if you are both of equal outputs.

Double Marathon

This is a brilliant design offering support to both front and rear. The head tube to rear bottom-bracket lateral supports the front seat tube low down, so assisting the down tube. The rear half of the frame is served by two lateral tubes and additional mid-stays in the rear triangle add rearend stiffness. The design looks like a five-bar gate but lighter gauge tubes can be used resulting in a frame of similar weight to the direct lateral but with superior characteristics. This design is ideal for expedition tandems, not only because of its strength and sure-handling, but also because dozens of bottle cages can be brazed on; there are just so many tubes. This design works especially well with long, rear top tubes, and by long I mean 26–28in.

To date I have built more double marathon tandems than all the other designs added together. I highly recommend them. The design is so efficient that

super light tubes can be used, such as Reynolds 753R and I often mix tubes from Reynolds and Columbus in the creation of double-marathon racing and *randonnée* frames. Please do not dismiss the double marathon simply because it looks heavy.

Double Marathon Lady Back

Historically lady back tandems have received bad press. The arguments are similar to those relevant to the women's solo frame; in other words, have a double men's tandem frame if you can. I know some women will not put up with a cross bar, so here is the solution. The design does work and in fact can be better than

Fig 72   A double marathon lady back tandem.

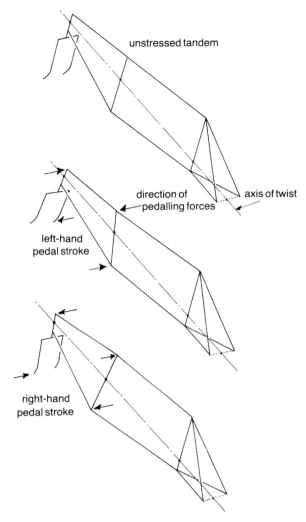

Fig 73 Axis of twist of a tandem frame. A result of pedalling.

Further Design Considerations

Twin Lats

To put the record straight, I do not consider twin lateral tubes worthy of consideration on a quality tandem. I have been quoted as once saying that they are about as good as a lead brick tied to one's drainpipe. Well, perhaps a slight exaggeration of their ineffectiveness, but I still do not build with twin lats. They are good at doing one job, and that is to control bending, but only in one plane, the plane lying between the two tubes. The extent of control depends on how well and how often the two spaghetti tubes are braced together – normally not very often. A single full-size tube properly mitred and fitted will quite as efficiently control bending, and will also control twisting. The control of twist allows easier hill climbing and will result in predictable handling when fully laden on alpine descents. Exponents of twin lats say they offer remarkable comfort, the tubes allowing vertical movement to give the rider suspension. In theory this is true, but in practice most comfort comes from good fork rake design and big fat tyres. The effect of main-frame flex is only minor and, as such, is to be sacrificed in the search for efficiency.

Oval Tubes

Drainpipes have been oval for over twenty years. Some are round and there is a place for both as each has merits. Most tandem users synchronise cranks so that both sets of pedals are at similar points of their respective strokes together. In these cases an oval drainpipe is ideal, the action of pedalling together eliminating most of the torque forces within the pipe.

some of the simpler double men's designs. It scores highly when the captain is tall, large frame size, and the stoker much smaller, say, a 25in/20in combination. As with a women's solo the rear mid-stays lend excellent support for braze-on centre-pull brakes. I have no hesitation in recommending this design and I have made a considerable number, including the very first Tony Oliver tandem.

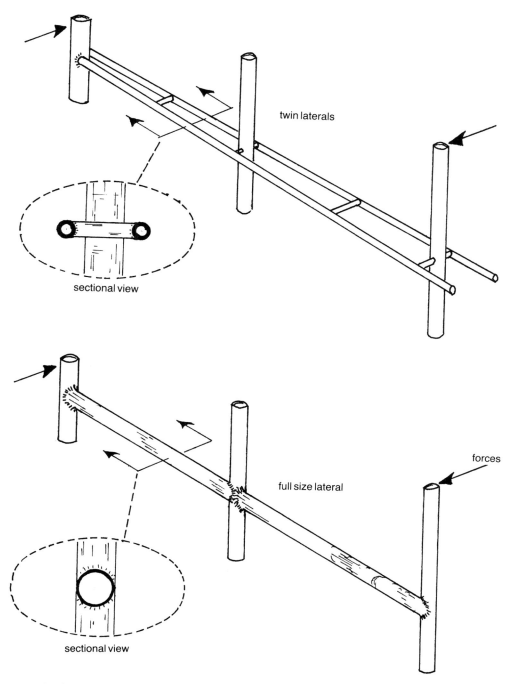

twin laterals

sectional view

full size lateral

forces

sectional view

Fig 74   Lateral tubes along twist axis. The full size lateral tube is about five times stiffer to torque than the twin lateral design. But it offers equal bending resistance in the horizontal plane.

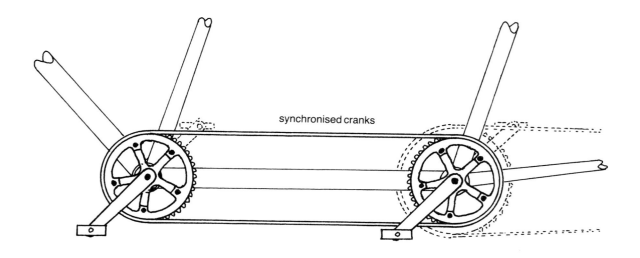

synchronised cranks

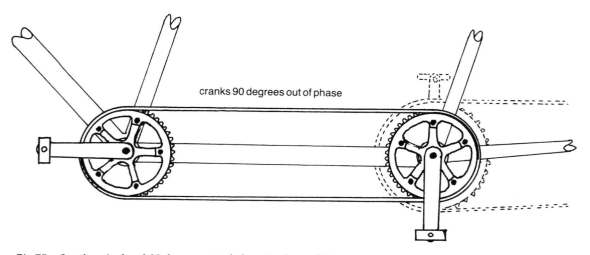

cranks 90 degrees out of phase

Fig 75   *Synchronised and 90 degrees out-of-phase tandem pedal arrangements.*

There is some thought that having the two pedal sets 90 degrees out of phase minimises pedalling pulses on the drive chain. It eliminates the ability to honk (pedal out of the saddle) but it does create a twisting couple within the drainpipe, a force handled well by its being round. Reynolds offer both round and oval drainpipes. The round version is heavy, having a wall thickness of 1.2mm. The oval drainpipe is thinner and ½lb (227g) lighter, with a wall thickness of 0.9mm. Many cyclists prefer the look of the oval drainpipe, so fashion may come into your compromise equation. I like to leave round drainpipes for heavy use – expedition and ATB tandems. The vast majority of custom tandems look, and are, better with the oval option. In the early eighties Reynolds, in error, produced all their oval drainpipes in the heavy gauge. These were great for tourists although not so for light racing. I hoarded these drainpipes as I knew they were a one-off; sadly, I have just used the last.

Some builders offer oval lateral and top tubes. I am not convinced of their effectiveness for the same reasons that twin laterals are inadequate. Oval tubes offer superior bending resistance in one plane only, at the expense of having inferior qualities in other planes and inferior resistance to twist. They are not as bad as twin lateral tubes; in fact I do not think they are much worse than round tubes, but they certainly are not any better. The arguments of comfort I again maintain to be invalid.

Forks

Tandems create some pretty hefty forces on the front fork so thicker gauges and/or bigger section fork blades are generally used. The exception can be a racing tandem where standard Reynolds 531ST fork blades are adequate. For heavy touring and expedition use, mountain-bike fork blades are used with their large oval section of 30mm × 20mm. The introduction of a new breed of bike – the city bike – has led to the manufacture of ideal tandem

Fig 76   Ugly but effective Columbus 32 × 22mm fork crown.

85

fork crowns, those slightly wider than the traditional Cinelli style yet narrower than the full width ATB fork crown. Reynolds make 531 fork blades in three cross-sections: 31mm × 18mm; the solo-size fat oval, 29mm × 18mm; and the ATB section, 30mm × 20mm. Columbus offer two alternative formats, 35mm × 22mm and 32mm × 22mm.

Life is complicated with such a choice. Unfortunately, decent crowns for two of the options – the Reynolds 31mm × 18mm and the Columbus 35mm × 22mm – are not available. The only crown for the smaller Columbus oval is a rather ugly, although very effective, two plate affair that costs a fortune.

The solo size Reynolds 531 option allows all sorts of quality cast solo crowns

to be used. These blades are perfectly adequate for most tandems and are often selected even for heavy use. If you choose a front disc or hub brake (*see* section on tandem brakes), ATB blades are recommended; not the unicrown version but the old-fashioned wide fork crown, preferably cast, and 30mm × 20mm. For use with a front screw-on hub brake, such as the Arai, the front fork-ends should be 126mm between faces, so the brake can be mounted on a standard rear hub.

Head Tube

Here again there are several options. Standard solo tubing (31.7mm diameter and 0.9mm wall thickness) is normally adequate unless construction is lugless.

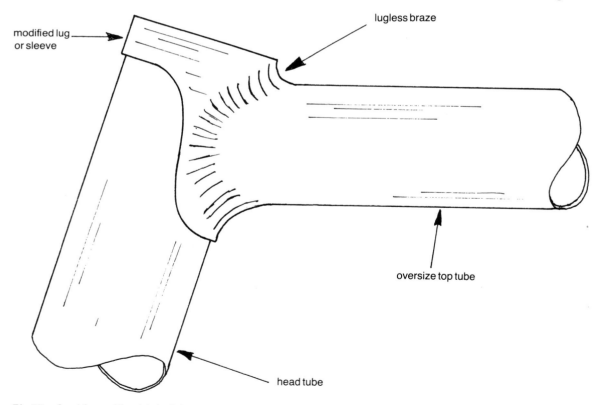

Fig 77 *Semi-lugged head-tube joint.*

Fig 78   *Semi-lugged head tube on a 20/19in marathon tandem frame.*

Lugged or semi-lugged construction is preferred for long-term reliability. Semi-lugged construction is time consuming and therefore expensive but, I feel, worth the effort. It consists of the brazing of two sleeves or modified lugs to the head tube and then a lugless join of the top and down tubes to these sleeves. The advantages are twofold: the head tube is reinforced about the region where the head set fits which is vital since head tubing becomes so thin once it is reamed to accept a quality head set. The second reason is a little more complex. When you braze a simple lugless joint, say, top tube to head tube, heat is only applied to one side of the head tube. This makes it go slightly oval, just enough to cause con-

cern after the head tube is reamed. The reamer creates a round hole, so the resulting oval tube has very thin walls on two opposing sides and thicker walls between. When a sleeve or lug is brazed to the same head tube, heat is applied all round the head tube's circumference so eliminating heat-induced distortion and leaving a round hole in a round tube.

I now use oversize head tubing. It has been a long time arriving but Vitus market Cr-Mo tubing 33mm in diameter with a wall thickness of 1.5mm. This tubing is of sufficient thickness not to go oval when lugless-brazed and is effectively the same thickness as a solo head tube with a reinforcing lug. It reams perfectly to accept the standard cup size of a quality head

87

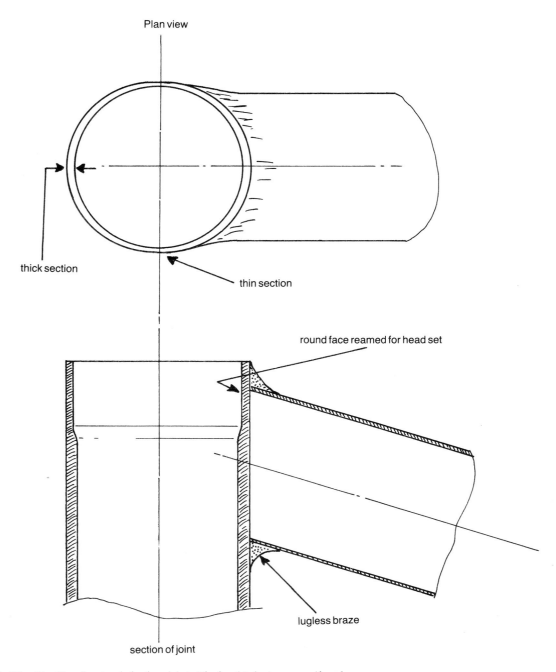

Plan view

thick section

thin section

round face reamed for head set

section of joint

lugless braze

Fig 79 Ovality of a simple lugless joint. The head tube is non-uniformly thinner after head set reaming.

set. In addition, I also braze on 33mm decorative external rings made by another French manufacturer, Bocama. In all, this set-up looks the part; it is strong and thick and will give decades of trouble-free service.

Dimensions for your tandem frame borrow a lot from solo conventions. Frame sizes should be similar to the solo bikes you ride but should allow compromises where partner sizes differ greatly. One point to remember is that a tandem top tube is lower than on a solo of comparable frame size, by nearly one inch. This is necessary to accommodate the front seat-pillar clamping bolt which is normally found on the forward face of the seat tube. Consequently the head tube becomes shorter than on a comparable solo. Touring cyclists adopt an upright riding position thus wanting high handlebars. The combination of a shorter head tube and high handlebars may lead to an excess of handlebar stem protruding from the top of the head set. This not only looks awful but is structurally undesirable.

Solutions are twofold: firstly, to have an extended head tube (although this also looks a trifle weird) or secondly, to have a sloping top tube (where the front end of the top tube is butted into the head tube at a point similar to where an equivalent solo top tube would meet). This is particularly effective if the rear seat-tube size is small: the slope can be continued through both top tubes to form a straight line from head to rear seat. On some frames of equal size front and rear, I have fitted a sloping top tube to the front only. It looks strange, as though the middle of the tandem has been crushed, but it is effective in allowing higher bars and separating the two races of the head set, so relieving their stresses. Specifying a slightly larger front-frame size will raise the top tube back to normal height but do not forget to allow at

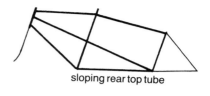

sloping rear top tube

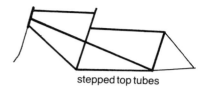

stepped top tubes

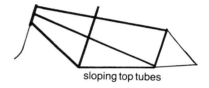

sloping top tubes

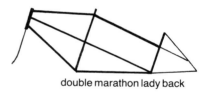

double marathon lady back

Fig 80   Common ways of accommodating large differences in front and rear frame sizes – beware of stepped top tubes.

least one inch of seat pillar to protrude above the top of the front seat tube – the rear handlebar stem clamps on here.

I try hard not to be controversial just for the sake of it and I know this topic will be for some. Giving the stoker a lower top tube is a common way of accommodating couples of vastly different sizes, but stepped top tubes should be avoided as they put a large, bending couple on the front seat tube – a thin, sectioned non-butted part of the tube. I prefer to see a double marathon lady back if a downward sloping rear top tube is unacceptable. Stepped top tubes are convenient with lugged solo diameter tubes; two standard seat lugs can be used at the front seat cluster with one upside down for the rear top tube, but I have seen several seat tube failures with stepped models, even when the two lugs are close against each other. A tight-fitting seat pillar should help support such a design but most tandems in 531 have 27mm pillars, these being only a second-rate fit offering little support. Lightly used tandem frames can get away with this step but not so for camping and harder work.

Seat-tube angles should be similar to solos but the head-tube angle and fork offset combination must not mimic a solo. I shall reiterate – a tandem must have neutral steering. If the tandem steers like a racing bike, it will leap into the hedge or into oncoming traffic every time the stoker scratches his leg. The steering must be insensitive to frame lean. This dictates minimal trail obtained with a steepish head angle, around 73 degrees or even 74 degrees and a long fork offset, say 2¼–2½in. It is odd that this combination is dangerous on a solo, giving low frequency cyclic handlebar oscillations which can be uncontrollable downhill with a laden handlebar bag. The tandem overcomes this instability by virtue of its enormous wheelbase and the fact that there is considerably more weight acting through the head set on to the front wheel.

These arguments are true even for racing tandems, a bone of contention with some of my fashion-conscious racing clients who loathe the look of two inches plus of fork offset on a racing mount. Nevertheless the ease of directing a full-flight tandem means the captain can concentrate more on the job in hand – going fast.

Top Tubes

Front top-tube length should be calculated just as the solo; there is no reason to differ. The rear top-tube length is not so easy. Traditionally, rear top tubes have been about 23in long. Today the vogue settles around 25–27in, giving the stoker much more room. If they are too long, the overall length of the tandem gets excessive; if they are too short the stoker can do nothing but sit upright in the saddle with the result of a sore backside. It is necessary to be able to move and take pressure from your seat. When you move, your body goes forward but if the captain's back is already up against your nose there is nowhere to move to.

I always advise that a rear top tube be on the long side if there is any doubt. If the result should be a little too long then a longer handlebar stem can be fitted to shorten the reach. If the rear is too short then that is that – there is nothing one can do except put up with the misery of being cramped and having the captain bang the stoker's knuckles at every stroke of his thigh.

On the technical side, I do not actually build to a precise rear top-tube length. It is the distance between the two bottom brackets that is important and this should be such that when a new chain is fitted the eccentric chain adjuster is towards the rear of its range. As the chain stretches there is plenty of scope for taking up the slack. Since chains are made with a half inch pitch the centres between shells should reflect this and be either a whole number of inches apart or a whole number plus half an inch apart, plus half the range of the eccentric which normally works out as one eighth of an inch. I therefore build bottom centres 24⅛, 24⅝, 25⅛, 25⅝, 26⅛in, etc. apart.

The rear triangle of the tandem can be

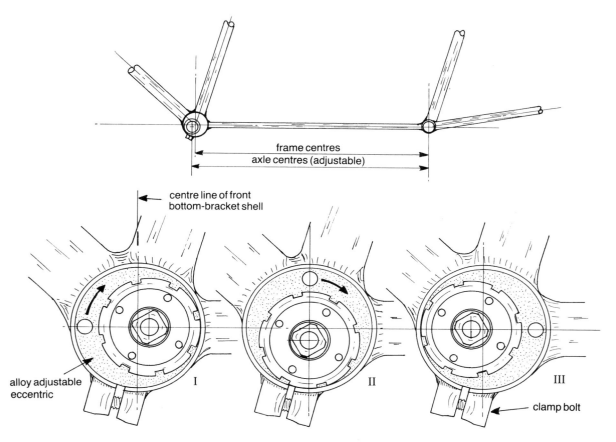

Fig 81 Bottom-bracket centres of a tandem. I shows the preferred position of the eccentric with a new chain. As it stretches, rotate the alloy eccentric clockwise (as arrow) through central position II to the position of maximum adjustment, III.

similar to a solo. Chain-stay lengths can be identical depending on touring or racing requirements. Vertical fork-ends are always recommended as these inhibit wheel displacement under heavy pedalling. It is also recommended that the fork-end spacing is 140mm wider than the solo 126mm standard. This allows dishless rear wheels, a must for hassle-free tandem riding and a standard that has found favour with tandem hub manufacturers. It also allows sufficient room for a rear drum brake if required.

All other aspects of a tandem frame can be treated as if a solo. Braze-on bosses should receive similar consideration but do not forget that oversize tubes necessitate braze-on fittings, oversize clamps being very rare. In addition, think about cable runs to all the brakes and which handlebars you want the brakes to be operated from. On direct lateral, double marathon and lady back versions the gear levers, if frame mounted, are often better placed on the front lateral tube. This gives a cable run direct from lever to rear

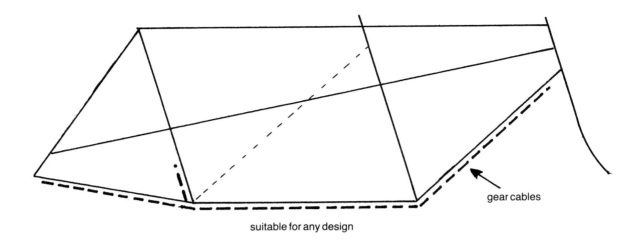

suitable for any design

gear cables

only suitable and recommended for lateral tandems

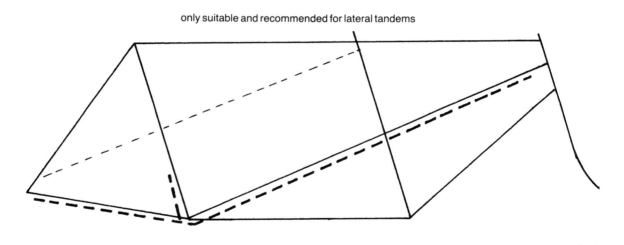

Fig 82   Suggested gear cable routes for tandems. Route on upper picture is
suitable for any design; the lower picture route only for when a lateral goes
direct from head tube to rear bracket.

bottom bracket causing less friction and
stretch. This is a nightmare for the frame
builder as taut cables lie in a perfectly
straight line. Should the two gear cables
running either side of the frame not be
equi-spaced where they pass the front
seat tube, the frame will be seen to be out
of line.

Tandem Parts

Components for tandem use are excellent today. Some need special attention but most items from the solo range work adequately. After buying a frame set, the two most expensive items are usually the wheels and a chain set (a tandem chain set). The theory behind bullet-proof wheels is detailed in Chapter 6 and is particularly relevant to tandems. Luckily forty- and forty-eight-hole hubs and rims are available and should be used. There are even a few forty-hole ATB rims around for off-road tandems.

The golden rule is, and I shall say it again as it is so important, dishless wheels. Fat tyres not only give a smoother ride but they also protect both rim and spokes from the majority of road nasties. I ride fat tyres despite being laughed at by trendies on skinny bone-shattering gossamers. I have been told my tyres are slower. In theory perhaps, but they escape thorns and I am often refilling at the pub while the trendies are still on the road waiting for their patches to set.

Chain Sets

Tandem chain sets come in many formats. The most common is the cross-over set-up. A chain connects both crank sets on the left-hand side of the tandem and a conventional final drive arrangement (with single, double or triple rings) drives from the rear right-hand axle to the block. Some riders prefer both chains to be on the right-hand side of the machine. This means that only two chain rings can be available for the final drive but it does minimise wear on the rear bottom bracket assembly. This is called a straight-through drive but it creates some unique problems. The two chains on the same crank need the chain rings to be spaced a

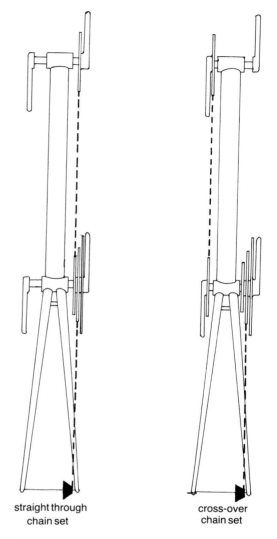

straight through
chain set

cross-over
chain set

Fig 83   Direct drive and cross-over tandem chain set configurations.

little further apart or the chains will hit each other. A worse problem is inner chain ring to chain stay clearance. Unlike a conventional chain set this inner ring carries the front chain, meaning more space must be designed into this area from somewhere. Straight-through tandem chain sets are more difficult to set up than cross-over sets and are not recommended except for track tandems.

Other riders prefer a cross-over set-up but with the final drive coming from the front axle, and with a very long chain to the rear wheel. The right-hand crank at the rear must be on a long axle to ensure it clears the chain on its way past. This set-up is a favourite with short wheelbase tandems where chain angle is excessive on six- and seven-speed blocks. It also allows the captain to see and hear if the chain is rubbing on the cage of the front gear mechanism. The long length of dangling chain must be supported on a jockey wheel mounted somewhere near the rear bottom bracket.

Quality bottom-bracket bearings are essential especially on cross-over chain sets. I do not advise sealed bottom-bracket units, even expensive ones. A quality, conventional cup and cone assembly will be cheaper and provide longer service. This type uses eleven quarter-inch diameter ball-bearings on each side. Most sealed units contain ball races, which on examination reveal only nine or ten ball-bearings per race but the balls are a size smaller as well. Less of them and smaller – what chance of survival being thrashed to death on the back of a tandem? While on the subject of ball-bearings, beware of prepacks calling themselves steel balls. Steel balls and ball-bearings are like chalk and cheese. Bearings are not only spherical, they are made from quality steels and are much, much more expensive. I recommend you buy ball-bearings with caution.

Unless specifically instructed otherwise I always supply cross-over chain sets with connecting chain rings of forty or forty-two teeth. They are normally supplied with thirty or thirty-two tooth chain rings which are just awful. With simple levers, the small ring puts a higher loading on the connecting chain, which stretches quickly and needs frequent replacement and tension adjustments. Large chain rings require more chain, the chain runs at a higher speed for the same pedal revolutions but it is less tense and so needs little attention. The immediate difference felt by the captain is the positive feel to the pedal stroke. Small chain rings result in spongy pedals, so you can feel energy being soaked up.

A positive feel from rings of about forty teeth is great in stopping unnecessary conversation. Initially partners tell each other when either wants to change gear or when gear changing is taking place. With time and experience this becomes automatic. You can feel your partner's needs through the chain; you know by the change in pressure that they wish to change gear or that a change is imminent. It is the ultimate method of communication and totally impresses others as you silently slip up and down the block.

Another subtlety of tandem chain sets is crank length. Nearly all tandem chain sets have 170mm cranks. However, if the captain is six-foot plus and the stoker rides a tiny 19in backend, having the same crank lengths may lead to continuous bickering over what gear each requires. The captain, whose cranks in this case are too short, will want to pedal fast to compensate. The stoker's pedal stroke will be exaggerated as 170mm cranks are far too long for such a short cyclist. He will want to push a high gear and hence the arguments start.

The French (TA and Stronglight) offer tandem chain sets with different crank lengths front and rear. I was staggered one day when I telephoned the export manager of Stronglight in France. I was after a tandem version of their 107TRI triple chain set. He asked me what crank length I required and then he asked me if the stoker was small and needed shorter cranks on the back. This is the way most tandem couples are, he said, so I settled for 172.5mm on the front and 165mm on the rear. This type of service is rare in the cycle trade; I was impressed. It may sound trivial, the odd millimetre here and there, but synchronising your rhythm can only enhance your enjoyment of the tandem.

Brakes

Brakes are debated at great length whenever tandemists meet. Both the types and the various arrangements for operating them stir many otherwise docile beings into opinionated fanatics. The reason for all this debate is simple: there is no one answer, no single ideal set-up. I am a committed idiot when it comes to descents. Drag brakes are no good for me. I must go like a bullet between each hairpin, braking sharply just at the last minute. Usually I get frightened first, which is okay because one of the golden rules of tandem riding is never to get into a situation that allows your stoker to question their confidence in you.

Most normal tandemists follow a more sedate path. On long descents, a drag brake keeps the tandem at a steady pace whilst two cantilever brakes allow fine control. This set-up is often achieved by using a rear drum brake operated by a gear lever, either ATB style on the handlebars or a handlebar-end gear lever. The cantilever brakes, front and rear, are operated by conventional brake levers. The disadvantage is that in an emergency only two brakes can be applied; not many captains (at least from this planet) have three hands. Some couples like the stoker to control the third brake, a nice compromise which can enhance the stoker's confidence.

My style of descending requires a front drum or disc brake operated from one brake lever and the two cantilever brakes operated by the other brake lever, a special lever designed to accept two cables. This is frowned on by many and I agree it needs strong hands. However, I have far more braking power available at my fingertips, and at all times. Any motorcyclist will confirm the difference in ability between front wheel brakes and rear wheel brakes. On rough mountain passes I can, even with only one rear brake, lock the back wheel. Not so with the front. My stoker (usually Christine) can, if desperate or just to annoy me, apply the rear cantilever brake by pulling the rear brake cable. I have open cables running down the side of the top tubes and it often settles an argument when I do not want to stop!

I hope that from all this on brakes you will conclude, as I have done, that only you can determine what is best for your style of riding. Be prepared to experiment and, if necessary, to have extra cable guides brazed on to your frame to allow alternative arrangements. The only rule I try and enforce is not to allow a stoker to control any front brake. The stoker will not be aware of the front tyre breaking away, say, on gravel – something that requires immediate release of any brake.

Head Sets

Tandems can be hard on head sets. The lower race takes quite a punishment and, in the case of a ball-bearing race, pitting can occur amazingly quickly. This makes steering notchy and is a problem with even the most expensive and respected of names. For better load distribution, roller-bearing head sets have proved most effective, particularly those from Stronglight: the A–9 and the Delta. You are left at the

Fig 84   Tandem trike front hub brake and twin cantilevers. A strong fork is needed and here is one: a cast ATB crown with Reynolds ATB 30mm × 20mm fork blades.

mercy of your frame builder as quality reaming of head tube and fork crown is the key to longevity. Again, fat tyres and small-radius fork rakes will lessen shock to the lower race, prolonging useful service.

TRIPLETS

The triplet, a bike for three (often called a tridem by the ill-informed) is rare, expensive and much sought after by cycling families. The first triplet I built was used for a family of four, three on the main cycle and one on a Rann trailer – a modified child's bike that is fixed to the back of a pannier frame like an articulated trailer. The second had a kiddy seat on the rear and a side-car for the family dog. He is trained to run up steep hills by the side of the bike and jump back into the side-car on command. It is an amazing sight.

Building a triplet is just like building a never-ending tandem, or so it seems in the workshop: there are so many tubes. There are two eccentric chain adjusters, usually in the front and middle bottom brackets and lots of brakes. Two drum brakes and two cantilever brakes make an excellent set-up. The variety provides four remote places to dissipate heat as heavy tandems and triplets can generate very hot rims and hubs. Otherwise, tandem philosophy is adequate although be prepared to compromise over top tube lengths, or your triplet may be too long to turn in the road! One problem with riding a triplet is the fine adjustment of the gear mechanisms: they are a long way behind the captain and it is difficult to hear any misalignment.

Frame designs do vary. Triplets are rarely ridden competitively or used for expedition cycling so fancy bracings are not normally necessary.

Fig 85   Stronglight A–9 head set with roller bearings. The huge contact area of the rollers gives long life to the head set, often a problem on tandems.

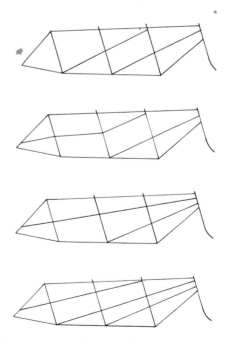

Fig 86   Just a few of the possible permutations of triplet internal-bracing arrangements.

97

TRICYCLES

Tricycles, or barrows as they are affectionately known, conjure up all sorts of ideas in the minds of non-cyclists. Unless you are disabled, few people can imagine why anyone would wish to ride such a device. I do not know why either, although I ride one. I suppose it is like mountain climbing. I have no reason for doing it other than it gives me a lot of pleasure. If you have never ridden a trike, you could be in for a shock. They appear to have minds of their own, steering the opposite way to what feels natural. As with a horse, make sure you tell it you are in charge, relax and all will be well. Cornering requires acrobatics but once mastered can be exhilarating; three wheel and even two wheel drifts feel electric. Traffic hangs back in amazement and usually overtakes on the far side of the white lines.

There are only a few trike-axle manufacturers in the UK: Ken Rogers, Swallow Cycles and George Longstaff. Other frame builders offer trikes but they all use axles from one of these three. There are few differences in frame geometry and dimensions between bikes and trikes. Steering geometry is best fairly neutral but not as extreme as on a tandem. Bottom-bracket height can be lower as a trike does not lean on corners, eliminating the problem of pedals hitting the tarmac. All you require is a little clearance between toe-clip and road when the pedal is in a near vertical position.

Chain stays should be shorter than those on a bike. For a start, there are no rear wheel clearance problems and also, bringing the wheels forward gets the centre of gravity closer to the axle and that means more stability on corners. The axle (the heart of a trike) comes in several

Fig 87   A tandem trike.

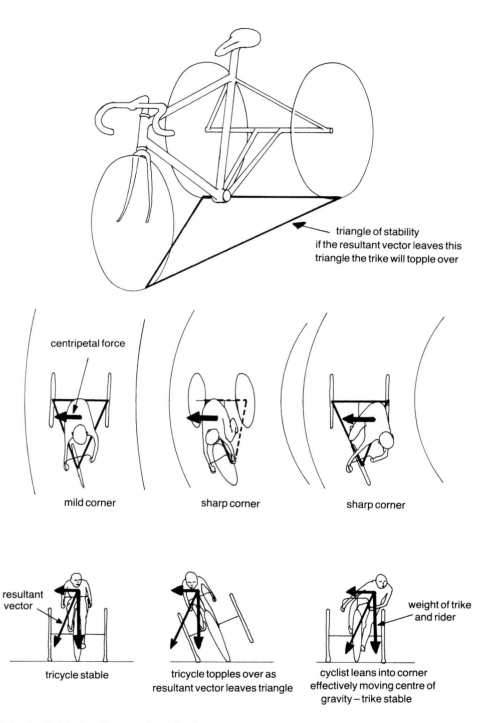

Fig 88 Triangle of stability of a cornering tricycle.

combinations of width and drive. Narrow axles are lighter but need considerable skill to prevent spills. Wider axles are obviously heavier but offer a more stable format. Tandem trikes have the widest of axles, usually around 32in. Drive can be on just one wheel or both wheels, the latter usually via a double freewheel. Years ago, differentials were made for the back axle and some tricyclists still swear by them. When riding in the UK a single wheel drive is not only adequate but, I feel, has an advantage. The drive wheel is through the left-hand wheel, lifting the trike up the camber of the road and preventing the perpetual struggle of steering out of the gutter. On the continent, and in France in particular, where cambers are steep and you cycle on the opposite side of the road, a left-wheel-drive trike is a permanent battle. Both camber and drive reaction send you right into the kerb.

Continental folk love tricycles – they are so rare outside Britain. I had quite a holiday one summer following the *Tour de France* around the Alps on a tandem trike, a single-wheel-drive trike at that. The French cyclists were amazed, even more so as we overtook them all on alpine descents. With only two not very good front brakes, there was no option!

Brakes, both disc and drum brakes, have been incorporated into rear axles. They are a bit specialist and not necessary on a light solo. Two brakes on the front fork are usually sufficient and can be in the form of a variety of combinations of cantilevers, side-pulls or centre-pulls. The problem with rear wheel brakes is twofold: engineering adequate support for the stirrups is difficult; and, even when this is achieved, the rear wheels lock too easily since they support little weight. Tandem trikes, with more weight on their rear wheels, can be effectively slowed by rear brakes. Side-pulls sup-ported on outriggers from the seat stays or drum brakes on the axles are two common methods, the latter being the favoured option offered by Longstaff, the most prolific manufacturer of quality trikes worldwide.

Tandem Trikes

These are the ultimate of beasts. The stoker must be very agile, even more so than on a solo trike. A trike will topple over when its centre of gravity exits the triangle formed by the road contact points of its three wheels. Solo trike wheels form a near equilateral triangle with the centre of gravity close to the centre. The tandem-trike contact triangle is long and thin, the centre of gravity much closer to the line of instability. Cornering and in particular braking on a corner, applies a centrifugal force through this point. If the resultant vector exits the triangle of stability, over you go. To counter the outward forces, the stoker must hang out as far as possible, shifting the centre of gravity in towards the corner. On a left-hand bend you keep your left foot in the pedal, grip the left handlebar with your left hand, hang on to the back of the saddle with your right hand and hook the cross bar on the back of your heel. It can be as frightening as it sounds, especially when you look back and see the inner tyre leaving the road. On hairpin bends it is hard work jumping from one side of the trike to the other and back again, but the sensations are wild.

Do not be put off by my description; I am a bit of an idiot downhill and so was Mike my captain. I was stoker on my only tour on a tandem trike. It convinced me that I wanted one, but not to captain. If you think you can handle a tandem tricycle take plenty of advice – a wrong decision will cost you a lot of money.

6 Components

WHEELS

The most common reasons for mechanical breakdown, apart from punctures, are wheels, spokes and rims. Hubs are relatively trouble-free although I still would not go on tour without a spare rear axle.

The wheel is built up of three components: hub, spokes and rim, and I shall deal with each in turn.

Hubs

A wise man on a limited budget will invest in the best hubs he can afford. They can be rebuilt time and time again using new spokes and rims. There are quite a few things to look out for when browsing through the range. I like nice, tight spoke holes with flanges of reasonable thickness. The spokes need to be supported where they exit the flange and they must not be a sloppy fit. This interface of spoke and flange is one of the single most important aspects of the wheel.

Figs 89–91 show three makes of spoke, a 13g rustless, a Magna 13/14g stainless tandem and an ACI 14g. You can clearly see how differently the spokes are shaped at their ends. The Magna has a longer curve than the other two and will therefore overhang the hub flange, eventually bend itself straight and then probably break. The other two, as shown by the 14g

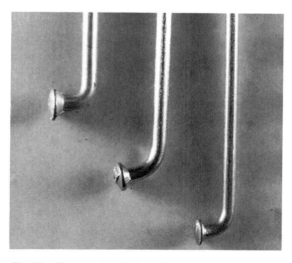

Fig 89 Three spokes. Left to right: a 13g Hipkiss, a 13/14g Magna and a 14g ACI aero. (Note the different shape to the bends at their ends. I do not like the middle one as it will overhang the hub flange too much.)

Fig 90 The Magna 13/14g spoke in a sectionalised hub. Compare how close it lies to the flange to Fig 91.

101

Fig 91   *The ACI spoke lies close and will probably last longer.*

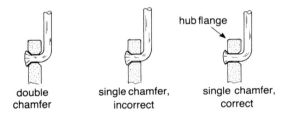

double chamfer   single chamfer, incorrect   single chamfer, correct   hub flange

Fig 92   *Spoke seating in single and double chamfer hub flanges.*

ACI spoke, hug the wall of the hub flange and consequently will probably last longer.

Some hubs have chamfered holes and it appears the chamfer is there to accommodate the bell on the end of the spoke head. Not so. The chamfer is to allow a smooth exit for the curved section of the spoke, hopefully minimising breakages. Most quality hubs have chamfers on one or both sides of the flange. With double-chamfer flanges there is no question which way the spoke should be fed but on

single-chamfer hubs, as shown in Fig 93, the spoke must be threaded through from the side without the chamfer. This allows the spoke head to dig tightly into the flange and be held rigid and will also allow the bend of the spoke to follow the chamfer of the hole.

I look for good, smooth bearings. I should like to be able to look for long-lasting bearings but that is impossible. Only time and experience will tell here, but I do not use sealed bearing hubs on my bikes and I do not recommend them. Sealed bearings usually mean ball-race units. They are tiny and incapable of offering the longevity of a quality cup and cone assembly. Strip a sealed bearing race and you will find the balls inside are smaller in diameter and fewer.

Ball races are intolerant towards axle flex and are in my opinion another modern convenience product, being cheaper and easier to manufacture. There are, of course, exceptions and some tandem and ATB specialist hub-makers use oversize ball races or will use two sets side by side at both ends of the axle.

Some sealed bearing hubs use special axles, ones with flats and lips that accurately position the ball races. Avoid these as spare parts are not widely available and likely to be obsolete next year. They also make it impossible to alter wheel dish should you decide it is necessary. Suntour is one sealed-hub manufacturer who uses standard threaded axles where the bearings fit on to threaded carriers that can be adjusted and moved in a similar fashion to cones. If you must have sealed bearing hubs, this type offers more flexibility and is easier to replace.

I do not worry about the pros and cons of small or large flange hubs as I do not believe there is much, if anything, between the two. If you like the look of one type then that is as good a reason as any to

Fig 93   A top quality, racing hub with alternate spoke hole chamfering.

choose it. However, if you are on tour, you may find it is a nuisance to carry two or more lengths of spoke in your tool kit. If one length will work for both wheels, spares are much simpler and you are less likely to holiday with the wrong length of spares.

I am appalled at the idea of having thirty-six spokes in both front and rear wheels. The old 32/40 combination was ideal but thirty-two hole rims wide enough for heavy touring are non-existent today. The 32/40 combination used spokes of the same length in both wheels if both hubs were small flange or if both hubs were large flange. Obviously, a 32/32 or 36/36 combination with identical-sized flanges front and rear requires iden-

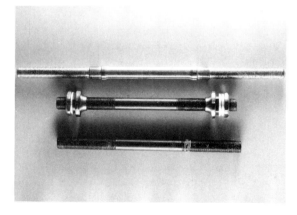

Fig 94   Rear hub axles. From top to bottom: a Susue tandem, a standard Maillard S700 and a standard Campagnolo. (The sealed bearing faces of the Susue make it a bit difficult to obtain.)

tical spokes. Good news for tourists is that a combination of thirty-six-hole, small-flange front and forty-hole, large-flange rear also requires spokes of the same length for both wheels. For those who do not want to carry spare spokes, there is the Hi-Lo hub, a hub with a large flange on the block side and a small flange opposite. These hubs are rare but can offer a stronger wheel, if laced to advantage, when a heavily dished wheel is needed, but more about these hubs later.

Spokes really work for their money. They come in three basic materials: rustless, chrome-plated and stainless steel; and in three basic designs: plain gauge, butted and aero. Dealing with the materials first, rustless, despite their name, eventually tarnish and the spoke thread and nipple oxidise into one immovable mass. Wheels with rustless spokes are difficult to retrue but rustless spokes are potentially the strongest. During the last ten years, stainless-steel spokes have become universally popular. The material itself can be a bit quirky and I have found some makes of stainless-steel spokes very suspect, yet others exceedingly reliable.

Stainless-steel spoke prices vary considerably; unfortunately, it is the expensive ones that give least trouble. One problem with stainless steel is crevice corrosion which attacks the spokes' integrity with rapid ferocity and is aided by salt. Salt comes from winter roads and the air near the sea. I live on the island of Anglesey and salt-induced spoke failure is common, although not with all makes. High chromium content spokes, the ones that look the most brilliant, suffer greatest. ACI spokes from Italy and DT spokes from Switzerland outlast all other makes I have tried. If you use stainless-steel spokes, of whatever make, keep them clean from salty conditions. The problem with the better stainless steels

and in particular ACI, is that they tend to rust a little if neglected. An oily rag after washing will make them look good and last a very long time.

Spokes will not last for ever. They usually break due to fatigue, a failure created by the cyclic application of pulsed forces. Stainless is a brittle steel and one with low fatigue resistance. It is not really ideal for spokes, this being the very reason stainless steels are not used for frame tubing. However, stainless-steel spokes are strong and I recommend them whole-heartedly; despite their shortcomings they are still superior to the alternatives. But they have a limited life and once they reach the end of their fatigue-life the wheel will soon collapse. The only solution is to replace the lot on a regular basis, perhaps every twenty to thirty thousand miles.

Chrome spokes are extremely brittle and should be left for light use such as time trialling. They are popular because they sparkle but they need to be kept very clean. Chrome is porous, allowing moisture to seep on to the steel underneath and rust. I do not recommend them for touring use; in fact I do not recommend them for any use.

Rustless and chrome spokes are available either plain gauge or double-butted. For tandem use, if you search very hard, you may find some extra thick single-butted, rustless spokes. Stainless-steel spokes are on offer in plain gauge, single- and double-butted and in an aerodynamic, oval format. DT also offers a flat spoke for the ultimate in looking weird, a design reserved for those obsessed with speed. Most spokes are 14 gauge (2mm) with their butted sections 16 gauge (1.8mm). For tandem use 13 gauge is common but beware of some single-butted, stainless-steel tandem spokes, marked 13/14g as they are not as thick as a true 13g and are made from rather brittle stainless-steel.

I recommend aero spokes for most applications, not for their aerodynamic properties but because once the wheel is built you can go to each spoke and visibly untwist the wind-up induced during building, something invisible with a round spoke. Their flatter profile also prolongs their life at the point two laced spokes cross, all-in-all building into admirable touring wheels.

Plain-gauge spokes are rather heavy for most applications, they lack stretch and for that reason should not be used with light rims. It is said plain spokes are favoured by racing teams since the breakage of a plain gauge spoke causes only a small side-to-side buckle of the rim – the rider can continue with little interference. That may be so but I would prefer to build extra confidence into the wheel from the start – to eliminate the cause not minimise the effect. Plain-gauge spokes just cannot be done up tight without the rim distorting. The spokes of a plain-gauge wheel will be relatively slack but slack spokes can also fail quickly. A general rule is to match light rims with light spokes and heavy with heavy. ATBs are fine with 14g plain spokes; Mavic CX18s are not.

Double-butted and aero spokes are so similar there is little to affect choice. Double-butted spokes are slightly lighter and can be tensioned to build a tighter wheel. Choice is often dictated by what is available in the length you require, a typical reason for making a decision. A heavier version for expedition and arduous work is the 13/14g single-butted tandem spoke. The principles are similar: they have the extra strength required where they exit the hub but are not too thick to be unresilient with a heavy, wide tandem rim. The single-butted tandem spoke alleviates the problem of not being

Fig 95 Careful enlarging of a rim ferrule with a ³⁄₁₆in 'sawn-off' chain-saw file.

able to pass 13g spoke nipples through standard rim ferrules, quite a problem with quality rims. Ferrules cannot be drilled out since they rotate as soon as the drill bit bites. Some spoke manufacturers have produced slim nipples in an attempt to overcome this annoyance. A fine move if you are delicate with the spoke key but the nipple walls are rather thin and once you attempt any pressure the nipple walls collapse making adjustment impossible.

If you use 13g spokes I recommend proper full-size 13g nipples. To get the nipples through the ferrules you will require a lot of patience. The only way is to force a tapered wedge through the ferrule and force open the hole. I have found

super champion '58'

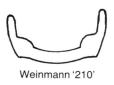

Weinmann '210'

Weinmann concave

box-section typified by Mavic

aero rim

Fig 96   Cross-sections of popular rims.

some makes of ³⁄₁₆in chain-saw file to be ideal, the ones where the handle-end gently tapers to a point. Do not try and file the hole larger, but hammer the smooth handle-end of the file through the ferrule until the hole is opened. Do not worry if the ferrule starts to rock loose a little, it will still support the nipple. Exercise caution, files are extremely brittle and splinter when hit off-centre. Wear eye-goggles and crack off most of the coarse file section of the file before you start. If you have not got chain-saw stockists near you, you will have to search for a tapering, round shaft of some other sort, perhaps a ground-down drill shank.

Rims

High pressure rims have improved a lot since the sixties when the Weinmann 210 was the clubman's standard. This was an excellent rim in its day but the design has dated. The most fundamental change is that modern rims have braking faces with parallel sides. This is essential because if a rim with non-parallel faces suffers a vertical buckle, the effective rim width will alter as the wheel rotates causing the brakes to snatch. This argument is still valid for ATB wheels as many ATB rims have non-parallel braking surfaces. Consequently I use Mavic ATB rims as they are parallel.

The next design choice is between the unique concave section from Weinmann, the box section made so popular by Mavic or the deep well section offered by Wolber in their Super Champion range. All these rims are excellent but some I feel are a little more so than others; so please do not be offended when I say I do not like Weinmann concaves, as they are still better than the rims of the sixties. It is again all a compromise. The concave rim is designed to tolerate vertical loadings but vertical loadings developed from pot-holes usually bend the rim flanges, whether the rim is concave or otherwise. It is lateral or sideways forces that cause spokes to be stressed to excess. It is, I feel, more important for the rim to exhibit self-stiffness to side loading so stresses can be distributed amongst more spokes and along the rim itself. If the metal forming the concave part of the rim were put along the base of the rim's cross-section, the wheel would be more usefully stiff. Box section rims such as those from Mavic are much more efficient at this job and I recommend these rims as first choice. The Wolber model 58 and 59 rims are a cross between the Weinmann and Mavics. They have earned a reputable following over many years in the tandem world – which is high accolade.

The best way to create a stiff rim is to have it wide. Trends are for narrow rims and, again, my thoughts sound old-fashioned. Rim width choice should be made in conjunction with decisions made on tyre widths and frame clearances. Narrow rims with fat tyres will cause the rim to attack the tyre's side walls where they spread over the rim flange. Con-versely, a narrow tyre on a wide rim will not work, it will simply blow itself off without warning. Aero rims are stiffened in the wrong plane just like concave Weinmanns. However, they are not nor-mally expected to do rigorous tandem or cycle touring work. They are finding favour in the fast touring circles such as Audax clubs and clubman's bikes (where they are ideally suited).

Anodising. There are many opinions as to the merits of anodising a rim. Some work in the USA suggests hard, grey anodising causes fatigue cracking as the surface layers affected by the hardening treatment are just too brittle. There is evidence to support this but I am cynical

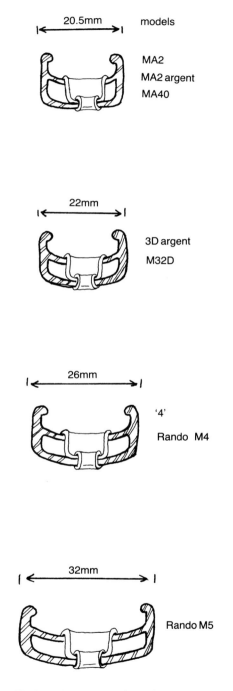

Fig 97 *Various rims sections from the Mavic range.*

of the merits of grey anodising for another reason: it is a pure waste of money. However, it does make the rims inherently stiffer (although not by much) and easy to clean. The latter comment is also valid for silver-anodised rims which only suffer a minimal price penalty over plain alloy and as such come highly recommended.

My theory is that the day you hit that pot-hole marked with your name, it will not matter about anodising as the rim, however expensive, will buckle at the tyre flanges. If you are on a limited budget, do not buy cheap hubs and flash, grey rims. Invest in better hubs as they will outlast many rims, be they non-anodised, silver or grey anodised. You can always upgrade your rims at a later date if you feel you must. You may consider, as I do, that silver-anodised versions offer good looks combined with long life at a sensible price (come join the small band of converts).

Brake efficiency is affected by some anodising processes, in particular models like the Wolber TX20 high pressure rim. This is an excellent rim and brilliant on a fast solo bike but the brakes are definitely impaired, especially when used on a tandem. For optimum braking, choose non-anodised or polished alloy rims. Silver-anodised rims come a close second.

Brakes and their continual use in dirty conditions, will wear away side wall anodising and eventually the side walls of the rims – even if they are expensive rims. When the side wall becomes concave, the time has come to consider replacement. This is quite normal, especially on tandems and winter touring wheels, perhaps as often as every twenty thousand miles. I am pleased when this happens as it means the wheel has given good service, the rim actually wearing out before having to be junked due to buckling.

Building Wheels

I do not intend to give a lecture on how to build a wheel. That is covered in several other publications. I shall talk about the number of spokes, lacing patterns, the number of crossings and last, and definitely not least, the wheel dish.

Hubs and rims are available in the following spoke drillings: 24, 28, 32, 36, 40 and 48. The most common is thirty-six spokes for both front and back wheels which is called 36/36. The rear wheel should in my opinion have more spokes than the front. This is because the rear wheel supports more weight, theoretically 55 per cent of rider's weight plus most of the luggage; the rear wheel transmits all the drive from pedal to road; the rear forks of the bike have no softening suspension, the front wheel being cushioned via the fork rake; and the rear wheel is dished in order to accommodate the block cluster and thus has a design weakness.

Back in the good old days, the standard was 32/40 when hubs and rims were sold as pairs in these drillings. The new standard, 36/36, has been welcomed by the UK cycle trade as it relieves stock problems. This attitude may be acceptable for play bikes but sadly it is also rife in the serious cycling sector. Forty-hole rims and hubs are available from most European manufacturers but not from many Japanese giants. Forty-eight-hole equipment has appeared for tandems, allowing the use of high-quality solo spokes for bullet-proof tandem and expedition wheels.

Even the racing fraternity seem backward in their attitude to spokes. Many buy racing wheels 24/24, 28/28 or 32/32. It would be much more sensible to buy 24/28 for time trials and 32/36 for road racing. These options are available from most

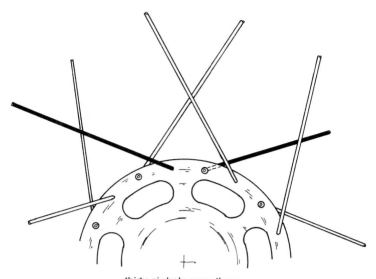

thirty-six hole cross three

neighbouring spokes form a 'V' (not tangential)

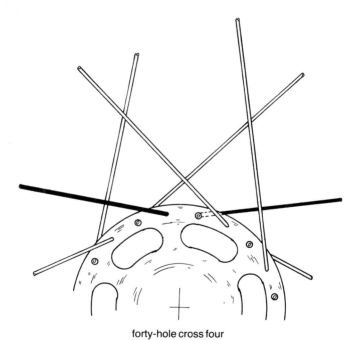

forty-hole cross four

neighbouring spokes form close to a straight line (tangential)

Fig 98   Thirty-six- and forty-hole spoke patterns.

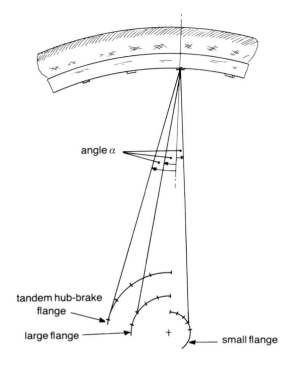

angle α

tandem hub-brake flange

large flange

small flange

Fig 99(a)   Tangential spokes and large flange hub causes problems at the rim.

No of spokes × crosses	angle α		
	tandem hub	large flange	small flange
48 × 5	9.7	6.0	4.0
48 × 4	8.7	5.4	3.6
48 × 3	7.1	4.4	2.9
40 × 4	9.5	5.9	3.9
40 × 3	8.1	5.0	3.3
40 × 2	5.9	3.6	2.4
36 × 4	9.9	6.1	4.1
36 × 3	8.7	5.4	3.6
36 × 2	6.4	4.0	2.7
32 × 3	9.2	5.7	3.8
32 × 2	7.1	4.4	2.9

Fig 99(b)

good bike shops although there may be a small price penalty due to the shop having to buy non-standard pairs.

Anyone who takes cycle camping or hard touring seriously should consider 36/40 wheels. It is not only the extra four spokes that make the difference, the lacing patterns between thirty-six-spoke wheels and forty-spoke wheels is different and benefit comes from the rim being supported more often along its circumference. There are some people who believe the more tangentially a spoke emerges from the hub flange, the less likely it is to break. There may be some merit in this when you consider driving forces alone. Practically, however, there are other issues to consider. The angle of spoke approach to the rim must also be compromised – if too far from the normal (90

degrees), spokes can fail at the rim end. This is common with forty-hole large-flange hubs laced cross-four. Similar problems arise with thirty-six-hole cross-four (a dreadful combination sometimes thought of as ideal).

Small-flange hubs minimise this effect since the spokes will exit the hub closer to the centre of the wheel. This is not a reason to believe small-flange hubs are superior – they are just different. Large-flange hubs of the same drillings should be built with fewer crosses, resulting in comparable wheels.

Wheel Size

The main contest in the eighties was between 27in wheels and what is called 700c. This latter metric sizing comes from France and is taking over. There is now a larger selection of tyres and rims in many styles and widths in 700c. The actual rim size is identical to a sprint rim so high pressure and sprint wheels can be interchanged without needing to alter brake block positions.

Historically, and primarily in the UK,

700c refers to narrow rim and tyre combinations, although the nomenclature 700c refers to a fat French tyre 700cm in diameter and 1½in wide. It is all rather confusing but luckily there is now a standard marking called the ETRTO, which refers to the diameter of the rim seat and tyre beading in millimetres, and can be used for both rims and tyres. The standard 27 × 1¼in wheel is denoted by 32.630. The 32 refers to the width of the tyre in millimetres, 32mm being equivalent to 1¼in, and 630 refers to the bead diameter, again in millimetres. All 27in wheels therefore use 630 rims. A narrow 1in tyre would be marked 25.630,

one inch being equivalent to twenty-five millimetres. (For other sizes *see* the Appendices.)

For small bikes there is a case for 26in wheels. The choice of both quality rims and tyres in the old British size of 26 × 1¼in is diminishing, so many are looking to the metric equivalent popular in France – the 650b. Mavic, Wolber, Rigida and Weinmann all make good rims in this size, sometimes referred to as 26 × 1½in. The ETRTO diameter is 584mm and tyres are available in sections from 25–48mm (1–2in) including a fold-up hi-lite from Michelin.

This wheel format is popular with

Fig 100   The author's touring mount: 23in but with 650b wheels for comfort and efficiency.

111

Audax riders and long-distance touring cyclists. The wheel being smaller in diameter saves considerable weight, a 32mm tyre and rim being comparable in weight to a 700c 23mm tyre and rim. The advantage is the amazing comfort of the fat, fine-treaded 650b tyre yet without the weight penalty. I ride a touring bike with

Size	ETRTO	Exterior (mm) [(in)]
600 × 25A	25.541	595 (23.40)
600 × 28A	28.541	606 (23.85)
26 × 1¼in	32.597	670 (26.38)
650 × 25A	25.590	645 (25.40)
650 × 28A	28.590	656 (25.82)
650 × 32A or 26 × 1⅜in	32.590	663 (26.10)
650 × 28B	28.584	640 (25.20)
650 × 35B or 26 × 1½in	40.584	661 (26.00)
650 × 42B halfball	44.584	670 (26.38)
700 × 18c	18.622	666 (26.22)
700 × 20c	20.622	670 (26.37)
700 × 22c	22.622	673 (26.50)
700 × 25c	25.622	677 (26.65)
700 × 28c	28.622	680 (26.75)
700 × 32c	32.622	689 (27.12)
700 × 35c	37.622	699 (27.51)
700 × 1¾c	47.622	713 (28.00)
27in × 22mm	22.630	680 (26.77)
27in × 25mm	25.630	688 (27.10)
27in × 28mm	28.630	692 (27.24)
27 × 1¼in	32.630	697 (27.44)
24 × 1½–¾in road	44.507	592 (23.31)
26 × 1½–¾in road	44.559	653 (25.71)
26 × 1¾in ATB	47.559	655 (25.78)
26 × 1.9in ATB	51.559	669 (26.34)
26 × 2⅛in ATB	54.559	670 (26.38)

Fig 101   A table of the common tyre diameters: for comparisons; determining bottom-bracket height; and use with small bikes.

650b wheels and it is responsive yet smooth. It is not as though I need to – my frame size of 23in is quite large – but I wanted the advantage of having slightly smaller wheels.

For 19in frames, these wheels are ideal resulting in a bike that not only responds like a conventionally sized equivalent but also looks like one. Availability can be a problem and tyres and rims need to be specially ordered. Some of the better wholesalers stock thirty-six and forty-hole Mavic and thirty-six, forty and forty-eight hole Wolber rims. Most Peugeot dealers should be able to get 650b tyres. Inner tubes are compatible with the UK size of 26 × 1¼in.

ATB wheels can be used on touring bikes, to brilliant effect. In fact I build very few true ATBs but I do get lots of enquiries and orders for traditional touring mounts with ATB wheels. Good road tyres are made, narrower than fat knobbly dirt burners, allowing standard chain stays and fork crowns to be adopted. For the rough-stuff rider this hybrid is ideal, having the weight of a touring bike yet with bomb-proof wheels. For tiny frames, 18in and thereabouts, they look about perfect. The cycle could of course be built with wide chain stays and fork crown to allow fat, off-road tyres if you wish, but the weight creeps up. A desirable side-effect of this is that the bottom-bracket height will rise by about ½in when the off-road tyres are fitted, allowing a little more pedal clearance.

For the international traveller worried about spares, the ATB size (ETRTO 559mm) is ideal. Most countries that have bicycles have ATBs so there is a good chance of finding something to fit in an emergency. This cannot be said for 27in, 700c or any of the 26in options as most popular countries specialise in making at least one size unavailable. There is a lot going for the ATB-size wheel, if only cyclists in general were not so conservative.

Dishing

The dishing of a wheel refers to the offset nature of the rear hub, necessary to allow room for a multiple freewheel. Bicycle frames are built with a symmetrical rear triangle, both fork-ends being equispaced from the centre line of the frame. The distance between fork-ends has varied over the years. The standard often associated with five-speed hubs was 120mm. The six-speed hub is now dominant and fork-end separation needs to be 126mm. Shimano eight-speed cassette-hubs and ATBs have introduced a new standard of 130mm – the latter in an attempt to reduce dish. Tandems have been using 135mm or 140mm for many years since their wheels must be dishless.

The problem with dish is that it introduces asymmetric spoke tensions. The spokes on the block side of the hub need to be very tight and those on the opposite side, slack. Consequently, equal-load sharing between spokes does not occur, the slack spokes being unable to transmit compressive loads and the taut spokes breaking, their fatigue life being shortened by higher tensile tensions and higher loadings. If you pick up any modern mass-produced wheel and feel the spokes, the block side will be solid and the non-block side sloppy.

There are two options. One is to reduce or eliminate the offset nature of the hub by using a narrower block, perhaps one with fewer cogs and/or wider fork-end spacing. The second option is to consider different lacing patterns on either side of the wheel. If short spokes can be introduced to the block side and long spokes opposite, tensions will equalise.

Fig 102 *Dishing on a standard six-speed wheel (there are seven sprockets – compact seven blocks are the same width as standard six-speeds).*

On heavily dished, time trial wheels I often build the block side with radial spokes and the other side with as many crossings as is practical. This is contrary to common practice and many 'style' wheels are built with radial on the non-block side and cross spokes by the block. This combination actually exacerbates the asymmetry of tensions, although it looks correct. It is commonly thought that tangential spokes are necessary on the block side in order to transmit driving power to the rim. In theory this may be true, but a time-trial wheel is not exactly highly stressed and, in practice, excellent wheel rigidity and trueness will have

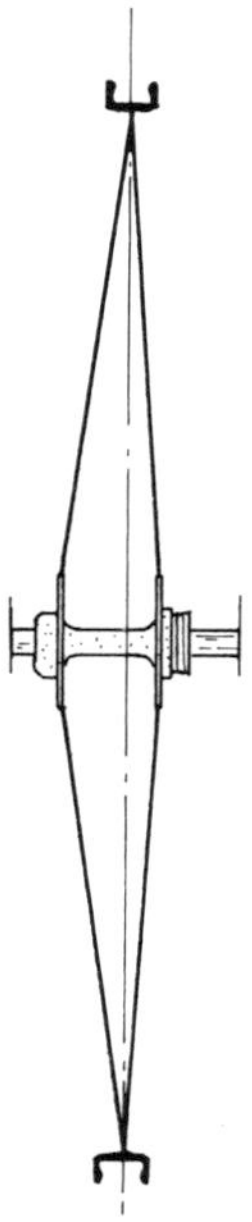

Type	Distance between fork-ends	Distance from frame to thread-end	No. of crosses		Tension ratio		
			block side	non-block side	small flange	large flange	Hi-Lo
Standard five-speed and six-speed hubs							
	120	30	×4	×4	1: 0.620	1: 0.620	1: 0.620
	126	36	×4	×4	1: 0.489	1: 0.489	1: 0.489
Specials for solo bikes							
	126	36	×2	×4	1: 0.507	1: 0.520	1: 0.524
	126	30	×4	×4	1: 0.776	1: 0.776	1: 0.781
	126	30	×2	×4	1: 0.805	1: 0.826	1: 0.831
Standard ATB widths, also suitable for touring							
	130	36	×4	×4	1: 0.574	1: 0.574	1: 0.574
	130	30	×4	×4	1: 0.897	1: 0.897	1: 0.897
	130	30	×2	×4	1: 0.931	1: 0.955	1: 0.962
Standard tandem width							
	140	33.5	×4	×4	1: 1 i.e. Dishless		

Fig 103(a)   Fig 103(b)   Asymmetric spoke tensions in a heavily dished wheel.

been observed. To compromise, dished touring wheels with forty spokes can be combined with cross two on the block side and cross four on the non-block side.

One elegant way of achieving tension symmetry is to use a Hi-Lo hub. It only works if you combine it with different crossing patterns left and right. The forty-hole Hi-Lo in Fig 105 is heavily dished, has cross-two spokes on the block side and cross-four spokes opposite. There are some schools of thought that argue, with the back-up of computer studies, that Hi-Los and asymmetric lacing patterns offer no advantages. This is true when you consider driving forces imposed by the chain but any system that can equalise spoke tensions will assist fatigue resistance, a property nigh on impossible to simulate with simple computer modelling. In practice, these hubs prove very reliable.

For most normal bikes with standard hubs the best way to eliminate dish is to rearrange the spacing washers of the hub. The standard 126mm six-speed hub gives a diabolical dish – the block side spokes being nearly vertical. If you are prepared to put up with just a five-speed or a compact six block you can move 5mm of spacers from the block side of the hub axle to the other side, so reducing the dish quite dramatically. I do this to ninety per cent of the touring wheels I build. Spoke breakages are minimal, rims stay true longer and complaints have vanished.

For tandem racing, quick release axles are preferred. This precludes the use of 140mm rear fork-end spacings as neither hollow axles nor quick-release skewers are made wide enough. Campagnolo market what is nominally a seven-speed axle and skewers, allowing fork-ends to be 133mm apart. This creates a totally

Fig 104 Unorthodox spoking for a time trial wheel. Radial block-side spokes and cross spokes on the opposite side equals out spoke tensions.

Fig 105 A Campagnolo forty-hole Hi-Lo touring hub. When laced to advantage it will minimise asymmetries caused by dishing.

115

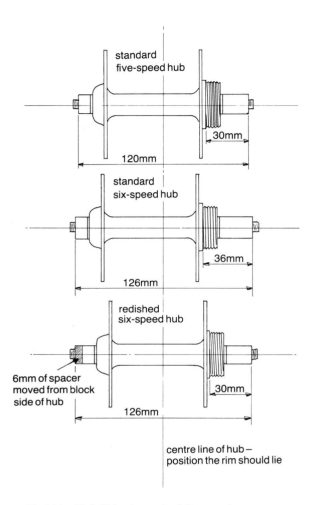

standard
five-speed hub

30mm

120mm

standard
six-speed hub

36mm

126mm

redished
six-speed hub

6mm of spacer
moved from block
side of hub

30mm

126mm

centre line of hub –
position the rim should lie

*Fig 106   Hub dish. A standard five-speed,
standard six-speed and the recommended
modification to form a minimum dish
126mm/five-speed hub.*

Most hubs with cups, cones and ball-bearings can easily be modified. Campagnolo market spare spacing washers in several widths, so fine tuning is possible. Rearranging washers and spacers is impossible with some sealed bearing hubs, those with dedicated axles – the ones where bearing seats are predetermined. Suntour is one exception: the bearings fit to adjustable seats and can be screwed along a standard threaded axle just like a cone. The instruction booklet for their pro hubs actually suggests rearranging the spacers to fit your dishing needs. All marvellous stuff – it is nice to see such a progressive attitude from Suntour.

When redishing your hubs you may need to consider frame clearance. The standard distance from the face the block screws up against to the end of the axle lock nut is 30mm for standard five-speed and 36mm for standard six-speed. These are the dimensions found on Campagnolo and other quality hubs. The makers of compact blocks claim a compact six-speed will fit in the same space as a standard five and the compact seven in the space of a standard six. This is not quite so in practice, unless the inside lower part of the right-hand seat stay is machined away to allow chain clearance. Most quality custom builders consider this at design stage thus allowing the chain to run a hair's breadth away from the right-hand fork-end. This is the ultimate in grabbing space in order to minimise dish and is without doubt beneficial. One point to bear in mind is that Maillard compact blocks are slightly wider than Suntour ultra blocks and so require about 1mm more clearance.

Another way to obtain dishless wheels is with an asymmetric backend, by building the chain stays off-centre with a matching wheel. This is a nightmare in the workshop but can prove to be just the

dishless wheel, if washers are rearranged so the hub will just accommodate a compact six block. The new vogue for 130mm hubs designed for eight-speed blocks will allow even more variants on the theme of dishless wheels. Although the eight-speed block concept gives terrible dish to the wheel, I applaud their arrival since, with just a little playing around, true dishless wheels can be made.

solution for some bikes. My 1986 Lapland special had an offset backend, off-centre by as much as 40mm. The rear wheel was totally dishless even with a compact seven-speed freewheel and a standard 126mm quick-release hub. The frame looked as though it had been under a bus and yet the wheels were buckle-free and had no broken spokes. However, rear pannier frames must also be modified to match the asymmetry which can be annoying.

Bearing Adjustment

Cones should always be done up tight; not tight against the bearings but tight against the outermost lock-nut. When tight, any spacing washers between will be in compression, reinforcing the axle to give an effective axle diameter of that of the spacers and cone. This is important on the block side of the rear hub as the axle is severely overhung, the bearing being well away from the fork-end. Most bent axles in this area can be attributed to slackness between cone and lock-nut.

Bearing adjustment is one of those tedious jobs. It never seems to come right first or even second time. Quick-release hubs must be carefully adjusted leaving just a little slack in the bearings. When the skewer is tightened against the fork-ends the hub axle will compress ever so slightly, just enough to tighten the bearings. Once adjusted, check bearing play with the hub tight in the frame. Solid axle hubs should be adjusted with zero play; they are not compressed as they do not have a quick release skewer.

Caution must be taken with many sealed bearing hubs. It is commonly thought that the axle nut next to the bearing unit should be tight against the bearing. This is not so. It should be just finger tight. However, it must be locked

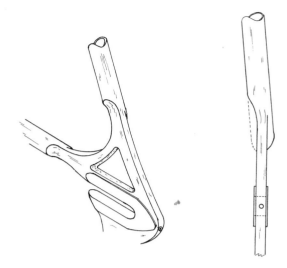

Fig 107   Chamfered seat stay to allow close running of chain to frame.

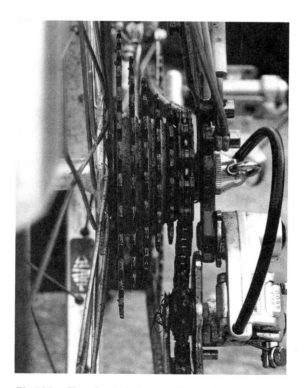

Fig 108   Chamfered chain stay allows the chain to run a hair's breadth from the frame.

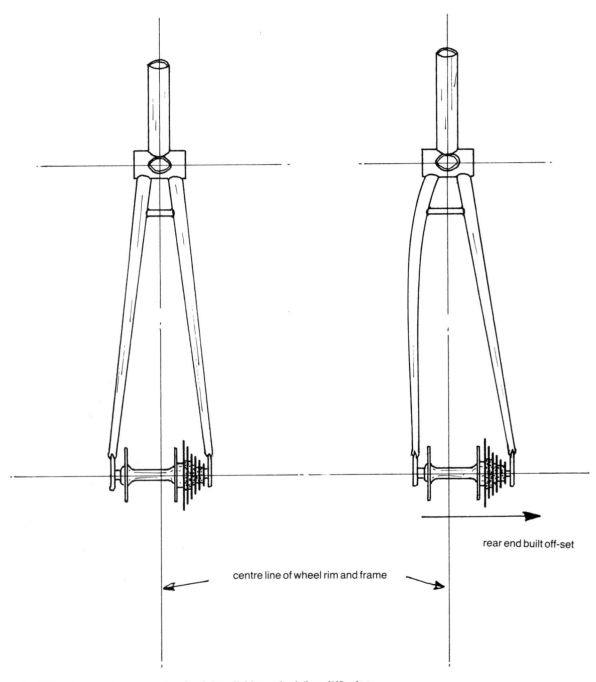

rear end built off-set

centre line of wheel rim and frame

Fig 109   Asymmetric rear triangle giving dishless wheel (but difficult to build).

tight against the axle-end nut to stop loosening. Many Susue sealed-bearing tandem-hub rear axles have broken because mechanics have tightened the bearing unit too hard on to the shoulder of the axle. This introduces severe tension to the very part of the axle that suffers most bending. The additional tension is enough to induce premature fatigue failure, particularly since these axles are rather small in diameter.

Tyres

Tyre choice is personal. Some riders with smooth styles may find that one brand and model will last, whilst another will wear out quickly. Other styles of riding determine other favourites. I have no strong recommendation and it is up to you to experiment with the various makes and designs.

For heavy use – the tandemist and cycle-camper – I recommend you avoid modern tyres with fancy hi-tech side walls. They absorb less energy and give a more responsive ride but they are fragile, making side-wall failures more likely. Old-fashioned gum-walled tyres can suffer from cracking but they rarely cause problems, their appearance causing more concern than is actually warranted. Side-wall failures can be attributed to non-compatibility of tyre and rim, the old problem of a fat tyre on a narrow rim. Match them carefully.

Mavic recommend their MA2/MA40 range of rims to be used with 19mm to 25mm tyres; their Module 3 rims with 22mm to 28mm tyres; and their module 4 rims with 28mm to 35mm tyres. These recommendations refer to European tyres; Japanese tyres of the same nominal size are about three millimetres smaller.

Fig 110   An asymmetric backend is one way to eliminate wheel dish.

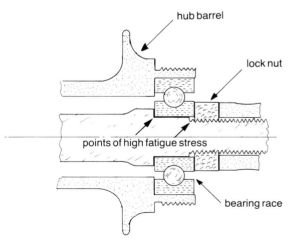

Fig 111   Sealed bearing hub axle and potential fatigue failure locations.

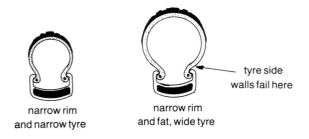

Fig 112   Narrow rim and fat tyre causes side wall problems.

GEARS

I refuse to debate the merits and drawbacks of hub gears and derailleurs. I accept, whatever the logic, or lack of logic, that some of you will only ride Sturmey Archer hub gears. I equally accept that most cyclists will not and it is for them I write this section (perhaps because I cannot think of anything to say about Sturmey Fives).

The gear train is made up of chain set, chain, block and gear mechanisms, front and rear.

Chain sets

A chain set is a complete assembly of crank arms, one, two or three chain rings and a bearing unit joining the cranks. In racing circles technical aspects of chain sets are not given much thought, usually 170mm cranks with 52/42 tooth chain rings are used – any make and model as long as it is fashionable. This sometimes reflects into the touring market but generally speaking tourists are more demanding buyers and are technically more aware.

Cranks are made in lengths varying from 150mm to 185mm. This is simply because we do not all have the same length legs. It sounds too obvious to be

Fig 113   A Stronglight 300LX triple chain set.

true and it is hard to believe when you consider that nearly all cyclists, whatever their leg length, use 170mm cranks. It obviously does not matter that much or there would be different attitudes towards the topic. The reason is that the body is very forgiving and will grow to accept what is wrong. I find it amusing that cyclists will often specify frame dimensions to the nth degree of irrelevance, quarter of a degree here, a millimetre there but never give a second thought to crank length.

I believe it is worth while to match crank and leg length. If your cranks are too short you will have ineffective pedal strokes overcome by always twiddling a low gear. Longer cranks for long legs will make more use of the extra leverage available. Do not, however, take this argument too far. A crank which is too long is just as ineffective as a crank that is too short. I know leverage is increased but the leg stroke must not become extreme otherwise fatigue will set in. The characteristic symptom of too long a crank is the continual pushing of high gears, an attempt to slow down the speed of the foot travelling its accentuated circle. An accentuated foot circle brings the knee too close to the upper body at the top of the stroke, the knee-joint is doubled up – an inefficient position for applying power.

Fig 12 on page 22 gives a guide to recommended cranks for a variety of inside leg lengths. Inside leg measurement is made in bare feet from the floor to your crotch. To do this stand against a wall, place a record album between your legs, firmly against your crotch and square against the wall. Mark this height on the wall and measure its distance from the floor.

Cranks other than 170mm are often hard to find and usually available only on expensive models. Such is the law of demand; 170mm are so universally wanted that they are cheaply churned out by the thousand. 165mm cranks are available from most manufacturers but 160mm and 162.5mm are available only from a few, such as TA of France. 175mm cranks have found a popular niche in the ATB world, I believe because they think the extra leverage helps on the rough. I am not at all convinced – the arguments I have put forward about bicycle crank lengths are just as valid for ATBs. I suspect it is a result of demand for large ATBs in the USA – a huge market fed by Japan and one which demands longer cranks for big, tall Americans. Over 175mm, and again your choice diminishes.

correct crank length

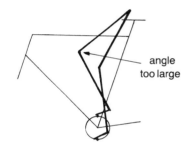

angle too large

too short a crank gives poor leverage

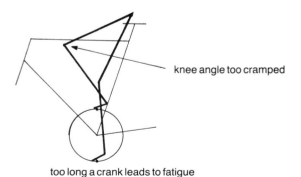

knee angle too cramped

too long a crank leads to fatigue

Fig 114 Crank length should be matched to leg length: too short or too long and crank leads to inefficient pedalling.

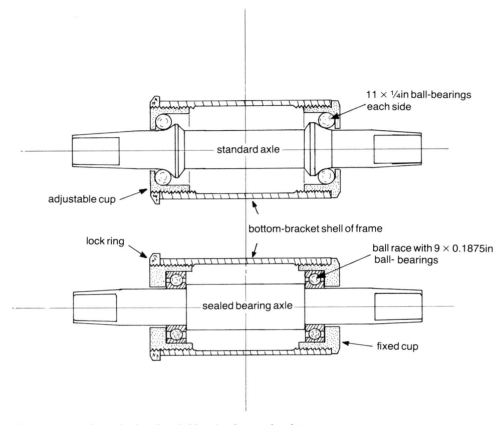

Fig 115 *Cross-section of standard and sealed bearing bottom bracket assemblies. Note the smaller and fewer ball-bearings in the sealed bearing race.*

Fig 116 *A cartridge sealed bearing unit, a Stronglight Delta.*

If you are thinking of changing crank length and have an opportunity to try someone else's cranks, give it more than just a few miles of trial. Even if you are testing your ideal, the change from what you have become accustomed to will feel weird. It takes time before you will settle and realise, hopefully, the change was worthwhile.

Bottom-bracket bearings can be a source of concern. Again, quality can cost but being an area of high stress it pays to invest in something pretty good. As with hubs, I do not recommend sealed bottom-bracket units for heavy use and particularly not for tandem or expedition use where reliability is paramount. The old-fashioned cup, ball-bearing and matching axle takes some beating. Eleven quarter-inch ball-bearings each side will out-perform a ball race having only nine smaller balls each side. I know dirt can get into the older design but even so it should be far more reliable.

Of particular concern are the designs that use alloy cups to hold the bearings, such as FT of Italy and Stronglight's 650 and 651. These rely on bottom-bracket shell threads being exactly square; if they are not the bearings run misaligned and fail in no time. These designs last longer in investment-cast, bottom-bracket shells because the threads are more precise and brazing heat causes negligible shell distortion. If you must have a sealed bottom-bracket unit I recommend the cartridge type such as Nadax, Stronglight Delta, Mavic, Edco, Suntour etc. These do not rely on bottom-bracket threads for bearing alignment and therefore have some chance of lasting a reasonable time.

Chain ring selection is another personal debate. There are those that swear by a wide-ratio double chain set; others, like me, a triple set-up. I shall defend the triple argument since most people managing to read this far into this book must be fairly keen on cycling and already have used a double chain set. I do not use a triple chain set just to have eighteen or twenty-one gears. It is there for convenience. I do not select the ring and cog sizes so each gear is unique, I cannot be bothered. I select a middle ring of convenient size, one I wear out quickly because I use it most of the time. The outer ring is there as an overdrive and the inner ring as a grovelling gear for those mad, but glorious days I venture into the mountains. The outer and middle rings are usually fifty-one and forty-four teeth, nice

and close to allow quick and accurate changing, even at night in the dark when I cannot see the chain.

A middle ring of this size also ensures that the chain will not rub on the inside of the outer ring, allowing the use of all six or seven cogs on the block. A larger than normal middle ring also makes it easier for the gear mechanism to derail the chain onto the inner ring (in my case usually thirty teeth) removing the possibility of the chain going too far and falling onto the bottom-bracket shell. It also helps in raising the chain back from the inner ring to the middle ring. All told, a 51/44/30 chain set, or thereabouts, is totally trouble free giving a number of convenient gears.

Americans have a fetish for what is called a half-step-plus-granny set-up. It is catching on here and is a theoretician's delight. The idea is to have the outer and middle rings close, to give a gear change equal to half that of changing one cog at the block; the tiny inner ring is for going very slow, hence the reference I believe, to a granny. Typically these chain sets are 52/47/26 and they are now so popular special front gear mechanisms are available to accommodate their subtleties. I have tried it but I prefer my forty-four tooth middle ring, simply because I find it more useful, the forty-seven tooth being just too large – luckily we are all different.

Without doubt the worst triple set-up is the standard 52/42/32 or 50/40/30. The middle ring is just too far from the front gear mechanism's cage resulting in slow or even non-existent gear changes when under pressure. It is particularly difficult to derail the chain between inner and middle rings. The key to a good triple is to keep the outer and middle rings about eight teeth apart.

Oval chain rings need a mention. I have nothing against them and again it is up to you to decide whether they are your cup

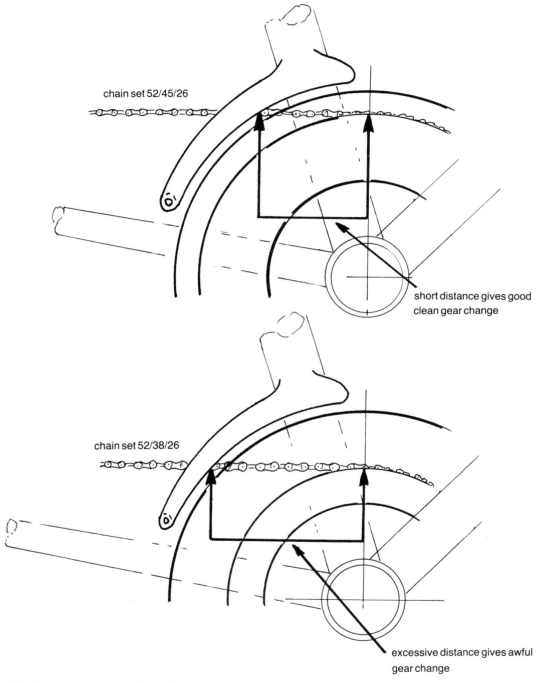

chain set 52/45/26

short distance gives good
clean gear change

chain set 52/38/26

excessive distance gives awful
gear change

*Fig 117   Keeping the outer and middle chain rings of a triple chain set close
gives better derailing and eliminates chain/chain ring rub.*

of tea. Unfortunately, that can be expensive; chopping and changing is not cheap; and I do not know if they are any better or not. The advertisements tell you positive reasons why you will be a lesser cyclist without them so I looked for advice from long distance cyclists – the Audax riders. Endurance riders do experiment and buy new ideas, yet a lot of them have tried ovals and gone back to round rings. Fifteen-to-twenty-thousand-miles-a-year riders must know something the advertisements are not saying. I admit to being not much use on advice here; I am still waiting to wear out my present round chain set before I start messing with ovals.

Chains

There is not a lot to say about chains. Most modern chains work and last well. Some indexed gear systems require particular chains to be used, according to the manufacturers, but generally most chains are compatible with most blocks. The only restriction is a standard width chain where the roller rivets protrude outside the side plates, which cannot be used with compact blocks. The only advice about chains is to keep them oiled. Modern lubricants work fine but there is still merit in old-fashioned oils.

I wonder again at the cost of spray chain lubs, two cans and you could have bought

Fig 118   A nice oily and long-lasting chain.

a new chain. That is amazing economics, although I understand some cyclists buy expensive, hi-tech chains. I am one of those heathens that uses standard Sedisport chains with engine oil. Ugh, I hear some of you say, oils attract dirt and the bike looks a mess covered in black gunge. Well perhaps this is true but my chain's demise is usually dictated by side plate stretch not roller wear. I clean the gunge off the stays once or twice a year, but with vertical drop-outs and an accurately made frame, wheel removal for punctures is a clean process. On long tours, particularly in mid-Wales, the Lake District or Scotland, where perpetual rain washes any lubrication away, I seek fresh oil from the discards of motorists. I go along to the nearest garage and politely ask if I can ferret through the waste bins and use the remains of oil cans. You must think me mean by now; perhaps so, but I cannot see the point of carrying yet another unnecessary item around with me on tour.

Blocks

A block is the name for the cluster of cogs and freewheel that screws on to the rear hub. There are alternative designs. Maillard have their helicomatic system where helical splines are broached into the block and mate with matching ribs on the hub. It is a worthy invention for serious touring as the block can be removed without needing special tools the size of a sledge hammer. Shimano have been pushing their freehub alternative which combines hub and freewheel in one. It, too, has its followers but there are none offered in

Fig 119 Maillard Helicomatic hub spline and block body allows block removal without tools the size of a tandem trike.

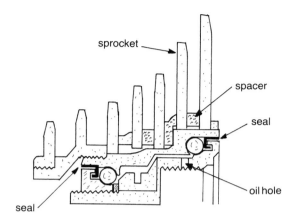

Fig 120   Cross-section of a Suntour New
Winner Pro sealed block.

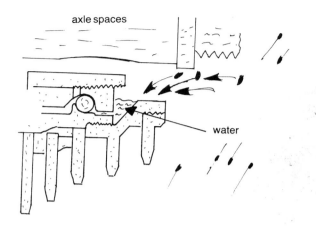

Fig 121   Overhanging top sprocket can
collect rain-water and road grime which may
get into the bearings.

forty drillings, hence its limited appeal for
touring. Suntour have followed suit offering freehubs for the ATB market.

Some blocks now offer sealed bearings;
these are ordinary ball and cone races
with labyrinth seals to prohibit dirt and
rain ingress – not to be confused with the
term applied to wheel and bottom-bracket
bearings. What an improvement, especially for touring where bikes get
abused in the foulest of weather. Sealed
blocks are highly recommended.

Many six- and compact seven-speed
blocks have the outermost sprocket overhanging the body. If this top cog is small,
twelve or thirteen teeth, any rain or
splashed water will collect inside the
sprocket and can then only drain out by
going through the bearings of the body.
Dirty water should not be used to lubri-
cate a block.

The number of cogs depends totally on
you. You may have decided to compromise and have dishless wheels which will
limit you to a five or compact six cluster.
Ratios are not within the range of this
book, there are yards of paper already

covering such topics, but there are subtleties to consider. Compact blocks have
their cogs physically closer, making gear
change slightly more delicate. If you ride a
lot at night, in a cycling cape, or on a
tandem where the gears are a long way
behind the captain, consider using a standard block, not a compact. The extra distance between sprockets, although only
slight, makes for less fussy gear changes
and less clanking.

Cog sizes are personal and I shall only
make a couple of comments. One of the
joys of cycling with a triple chain set is
that the wide spread of chain ring sizes
allows a closer ratio block. This argument
is directed at club and Audax riders where
speed is of interest, yet a wide range is
necessary for mountain events.

When in a hurry there is nothing worse
than gears spread too far apart; one minute you feel as though you are about to
stall; change gear and you are twiddling
like mad. An equivalent range of gears is
possible with a standard 52/42 racing
chain set but the cogs of the block must be
wider spread to give the same overall

Fig 122   Braze-on front mechanisms mean main-tube paint is not damaged.

range. My next point is again directed towards the faster touring cyclist. Cogs at the top end of the block, the smaller cogs, need to be close for similar reasons. A 13 teeth to 16 teeth jump is awful especially when attempting any speed. There are many ways to build up a 13–28 tooth block and here are two examples: 13–14–16–19–23–28 or 13–15–18–21–24–28. The latter is theoretically better, with more even jumps across its range, but the former is more practical with smaller percentage steps at the high end – the end used when going fast. The former will offer a sort of close ratio gear box at top speed and a wider ratio box for the harder touring parts of the trip. Combined with a triple chain set, you can actually select different parts of the block to suit the terrain and how you feel: middle ring and small sprockets give finer gear changes; big ring and large sprockets coarser gear changes.

GEAR MECHANISMS

Today's market moves with such pace that any details of specific gear mechs (as they are known) would be obsolete before anyone read this book. Therefore I think it prudent to consider general principles only.

Front Gear Mechs

These come in two basic versions: racing and touring, the latter with variations for different triple chain ring combinations. In addition, most manufacturers offer standard clamp-around-the-tube versions and braze-on versions. There is no doubt that braze-on versions look the neatest and in the long term are most practical – if you know from the start what size outer chain ring you want. Should

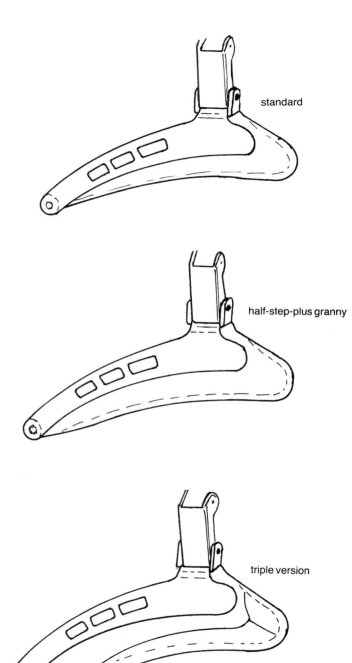

Fig 123 Cage designs of different front gear mechanisms.

Fig 124   Deep back-plate, Ofmega triple chain set front gear mechanism.

there be any doubt, forget them and have one fitted next respray. They do facilitate slight adjustment, braze-on brackets have a slot allowing for a range of about five teeth on the outer ring. That may be enough but then it may not. The trouble with clamp-on front mechs is that the clamp scratches the paint and on thin racing and clubman frames I have seen deformed tubes. Damaged paintwork does not matter on the braze-on boss itself (it is a large lump of metal) whereas the seat tube is comparatively very thin and part of the main structure. All commonly used braze-on front gear mechs now fit a standard boss – the Campagnolo boss. There are slight variations of height between some models but your frame

builder should be able to advise when fitting.

Racing gear mechs have short cages and touring mechs long cages to allow the chain to drop over a wider range of chain ring sizes. Racing versions are designed to work over a ten to twelve tooth variation in chain ring size and touring mechs anything up to thirty teeth. Triple chain set, touring versions have a deep back plate so the chain is easily lifted from inner to middle chain ring. They are very effective, boosting confidence and giving perfect changes. Half-step-plus-granny chain sets cannot use these deep plate mechs, the back plate fouls on the middle ring when attempting to engage the outer chain ring. As I said earlier, there is a

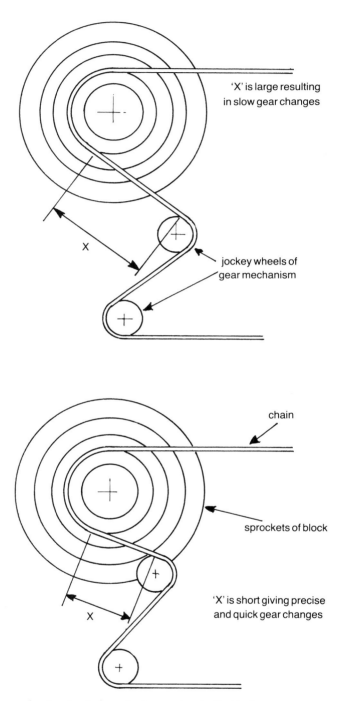

'X' is large resulting
in slow gear changes

jockey wheels of
gear mechanism

X

chain

sprockets of block

'X' is short giving precise
and quick gear changes

X

*Fig 125   If the rear-gear-mechanism top jockey wheel runs close to the block
sprockets, gear change will be quick and sweet.*

131

special cage made for these chain sets, similar to a racing mech but with a long arm to cope with the overall range.

Rear Gear Mechs

These have had to improve dramatically with the advent of index gears. In fact, index rear gear mechs are now so good they make index gear levers almost obsolete! A gear mech will give precise change only if its top jockey wheel is close to the cogs of the block. One classic example of an awful gear was the now obsolete Suntour Cyclone GT Mark 2, the top jockey was totally remote and so was the gear change. I can recommend almost any rear gear designed for index use, be it Accushift from Suntour or SIS from Shimano or Aris from Sachs-Huret. Choose a long-arm version if you have an extensive gear range and a short-arm version if not – life is very simple. I am so impressed, I only recommend click-click gear mechs, even if you do not wish to use their noisy levers.

Gear levers come in several formats: down tube, handlebar stem, handlebar mounting, and handlebar end control. Again, there is no ideal type. Down tube levers are most common. It means taking your hand off the handlebar to change gear but the cable is short and the gear change precise and quick. Handlebar controls need more cable giving less responsive changes but allow your hands to remain on the bars. The choice is that simple. If you go for down tube levers I advise braze-on bosses, Campagnolo style, for the same reasons as I like braze-on front gear mechs – clamps damage paintwork. If you are not sure about handlebar levers and you have already got lever bosses brazed to your down tube, search around and you will find little adaptors which convert the bosses to outer cable stops.

SEAT PILLARS

I disagree with many on the subject of seat pillars. For years 27.2mm seat pillars have been put in most quality frames without problems. I believe 27.4mm pillars should be used in most 531 frames, although not all. The internal diameter of the seat tube can be calculated by measuring the outside diameter and subtracting the thicknesses of the two side walls. All imperial tubed frames have seat tubes with an outside diameter of 28.6mm (1⅛in). The wall thickness of the seat tube of all the following is 0.55mm: 531c, 531Pro, 653, 753, most 531STs and the old 531db. Taking away two wall thicknesses gives an internal diameter of 27.5mm. A 0.1mm clearance is ideal and 27.4mm seat pillars fit beautifully in the above frames when the seat cluster is silver brazed i.e. not distorted.

Most 531 frames are brass brazed, a process at a higher temperature where the thin seat tube distorts just a little. This does not hurt its strength but effectively makes the internal hole size smaller. The tube is then reamed with a 27.2mm reamer, hence the normally quoted size is used. That is fine but the fit is only second-rate and inevitably water creeps into the gap. Alloy seat pillars have a nasty habit of corroding into seat tubes.

Fig 126 shows seat tube dimensions for various tube sets together with recommended pillar diameters for both brass-brazed frames (i.e. normally accepted sizes) and those frames built to higher standards with minimal distortion. Do not take the latter case too earnestly: there are exceptions, genuine exceptions where other sizes fit. For example, 753R can vary because the heat process of converting it from 531 can cause slight ovality of the thin seat tube. I have yet to find such a case and all my 753R frames

Tube	Wall thickness (mm)	Internal diameter (mm)	Seat pillar size	
			brazed frame (mm)	silver brazed to highest standards (mm)
Columbus				
Max	0.5	27.6	27.4	27.6
TSX	0.6	27.4	27.2	27.4
SL/SLX	0.6	27.4	27.2	27.4
SP/SPX	0.7	27.2	27.0	27.2
Cromor	0.6	27.4	27.2	27.4
OR and MAX OR	0.6	27.4	27.2	27.4
Cromor OR	0.7	27.2	27.0	27.2
Tandem CM	0.7	27.2	27.0	27.2
Tandem CR	0.6	27.4	27.2	27.4
Reynolds				
753	0.55	27.5	—	27.4
708	0.6	27.4	27.2	27.4
653 & 531C	0.55	27.5	27.2	27.4
531ST	0.7	27.2	27.0	27.2
525 & 525T	0.6	27.4	27.2	27.4
753AT	0.55	27.5	—	27.4
653AT	0.55	27.5	27.2	27.4
531AT & 501AT	0.7	27.2	27.0	27.2
531 Magnum	0.7	30.35	30.2	—
753 Tandem	0.7	27.2	—	27.2
531 Tandem	0.7	27.2	27.0	27.2
Tange				
Prestige SuperLite	0.6	27.4	27.2	27.4
Prestige	0.6	27.4	27.2	27.4
No.1, No.2 & No.3	0.9	26.8	26.6	26.8
Infinity	0.6	27.4	27.2	27.4
Prestige Concept MTB	0.6	27.4	27.2	27.4
Prestige MTB	0.6	27.4	27.2	27.4
MTB	0.7	27.2	27.0	27.2
Infinity MTB	0.7	27.2	27.0	27.2
Vitus				
GTI & TXO	0.6	27.4	27.2	27.4
Olympic	0.8	27.0	26.8	27.0
Rocky ATB	0.8	27.0	26.8	27.0

Note: Reynolds 753 should only be silver brazed; Reynolds 531 Magnum uses over-size seat tube; Columbus Max needs a 27.6mm seat pillar but nobody makes one!

Fig 126   Table of seat pillar sizes for both normal and top-quality built frames.

have been delivered with 27.4mm seat pillars.

I have found examples of tube with slightly thicker walls than quoted values.

They still lie within the tolerance range of the tube spec but they require a size smaller seat pillar. 27.4mm pillars are in many manufacturers' catalogues, but the only models I have actually been able to obtain are Campagnolo, JPR and Stronglight.

Some frames are made with metric diameter tubes, including most French models such as Peugeot. Metric frames need seat pillars 0.6mm smaller in diameter, so beware – there are a few anomalies. Another confusing factor is that seat pillar diameters vary considerably. A pillar may be marked 27.2mm but it could be as much as 0.2mm out, either larger or smaller. For this reason, I like to supply a seat pillar with all my new frame sets so I can select the best one to fit the seat tube.

Do not use the wrong size seat pillar. If it is too large it simply will not fit but if it is too small the clamp bolt will be over-stressed, the frame tube will distort and water ingress occur. A correctly fitting seat pillar in a beautifully prepared frame will slide like a silky piston. The closer fit of such a combination will not allow water to intrude, but both frame and pillar should be greased before assembly.

If you are unfortunate enough to have a seat pillar stuck in a frame do *not* apply heat. Aluminium expands about three times as much as steel, so heating will only make it stick tighter. Place the frame into the freezer or the seat pillar into a bucket of ice. Once it is really cold, place the pillar in a big vice, get a cloth, soak it in hot water and as soon as you wrap it around the seat tube, twist the frame in the vice. You must be quick since the pillar will soon absorb heat. Once this has happened you must stop and refreeze it. A terrible job to have to do, so keep your seat pillars cleaned and greased.

HEAD SETS

The longevity of any head set is dependent on how precisely your frame has been finished. If the faces on both head tube and fork crown are not perfectly square to each other, there will be unequal loading on the ball-bearings and it will pit. There is nothing worse than a notchy head set for making the bike feel strange. If you are going through head sets quickly have a Campagnolo tool set check out your faces.

Choice of head set is personal. Most models give acceptable service but for practical reasons consider one of the many sealed versions about. I favour Stronglight models, the ones with small roller bearings held in polyamide cages. They seem to last extremely well and spare parts are easily available via their importer.

Not all head sets are dimensioned the same. This causes a lot of aggravation but is a problem associated more with older frames. Modern head sets, in the quality range, follow standard Campagnolo dimensions: 30.2mm frame cups, 26.4mm fork cone and a stack height of 39mm. The frame cups are the two pieces that fit into the head tube. Their diameter is 30.2mm and the frame must be reamed slightly smaller – 30.0mm to give a good tight interference fit. The fork cone fits over the steering column of the fork and is also a tight fit, the cone being 26.4mm in diameter and the fork seat 26.5mm. The stack height is how much longer the steering column has to be over the length of the head tube to accommodate the bearing assemblies.

Older designs of head set used various other combinations of size and height. If your steering column is only 30mm or 35mm longer than the head tube, a modern head set will probably not fit. Again, there are exceptions – track head sets, for example, use a 35mm stack height. They are rarely used but can be of use if the steering column is short and a quality head set is required for an old frame. If buying a replacement head set, seek some expert advice, preferably that of a frame builder.

Head sets should be fitted with care, with proper pressing tools, *not* a hammer. I have seen bike test reports stating that the head set worked loose, a normal phenomenon as it settles down. This is not so – a properly pressed in and properly adjusted head set should not need further adjustment for tens of thousands of miles. There is no excuse for slack bearings after a few miles, except bone idleness.

BRAKES

Brakes fall into two basic categories: rim brakes and hub brakes. Rim brakes are the most common, being lighter and generally adequate for most cyclists. Hub brakes are used on ATBs and tandems either as a drum or a disc. The idea of hub brakes on a tandem is that it provides an alternative place to deposit heat, as considerable heat is generated on long descents.

Rim brakes are available in side-pull, centre-pull and cantilever versions, each having a place on some sort of bike. Side-pull brakes have found favour with lighter racing and clubman-style riders. They have a rather low mechanical advantage and, as such, feel more solid. They have ample power to stop most solo bikes but are a little wanting on a tandem. Brake stirrup depths have reduced over the years and modern, short-reach side-pulls are much more effective than the longer reaches of yesteryear. There is simply less metal to flex. I am amazed at the cost of some side-pulls. You should hear the number of cyclists that moan at the price of a true custom frame, yet they seem quite happy to spend equivalent money on a set of brakes! As with most products, there is a value for money curve where, initially, quality rises steeply with price,

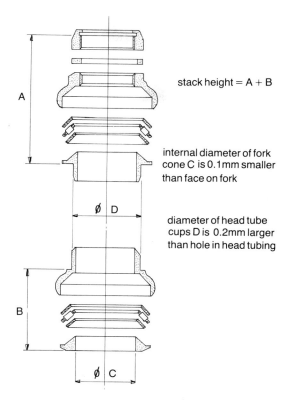

stack height = A + B

internal diameter of fork cone C is 0.1 mm smaller than face on fork

diameter of head tube cups D is 0.2 mm larger than hole in head tubing

Fig 127   Stack and reaming dimension of a standard size quality head set – in this case a Stronglight A–9.

then the curve flattens and you pay a lot more for little extra in quality. The ideal is to be on the knee of that curve. I prefer to see side-pulls on a lightly-used bike, cantilevers being too fierce.

Centre-pull brakes are out of fashion, although a revival is apparent on ATBs – they call them U brakes. Centre-pull brakes have a reputation for feeling spongy, which they do, but it is because they have a high mechanical advantage. This means that it takes less lever effort to apply the same brake-block force on to the rim, but the lever has further to travel in applying that force. In short, they are ideal for cyclists with weak hands, in-

Fig 128   A Suntour rim crusher; a roller cam brake.

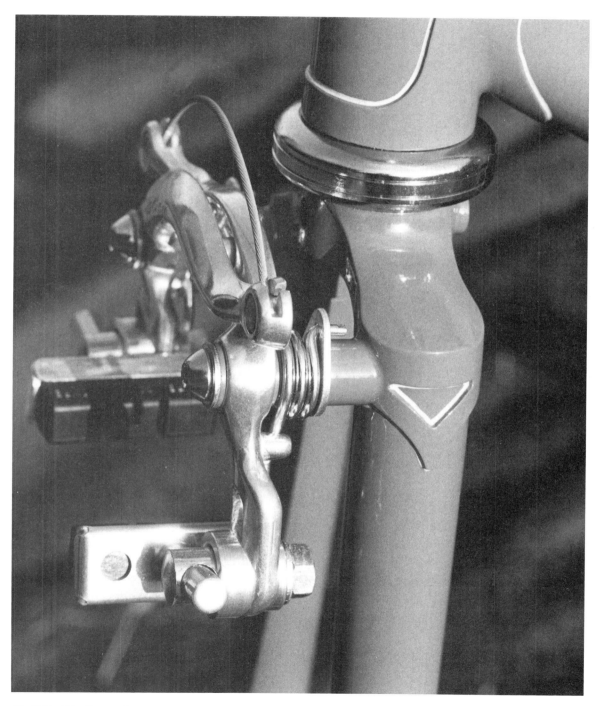

Fig 129   Dia-Compe, braze-on centre-pull brake.

cluding many ladies. The disadvantage is that the blocks must be set very close to the rim when in the off position, requiring absolutely true wheels and more frequent maintenance to compensate for block wear.

One way to minimise the soft feel of a centre-pull is to fit it to braze-on bosses, a popular format in France and the USA. It is the pivot carrier, the alloy arm that bolts to the fork crown, that bends most when applying the front brake. Replacing this with braze-on pivots, on the fork blades and seat stays, makes the brake a totally different beast – equivalent in some cases to a cantilever. The advantage over the cantilever, particularly on the rear, is that the brakes do not stick out and foul your pannier bags. They are, in my opinion, much neater than cantilevers but they have not caught on in Britain, perhaps because they are so hard to braze on. Inter-pivot spacing must be precise and the flats that align the tension springs must be positioned even more precisely. If they are not, the brake will hang unbalanced with one brake block rubbing the rim. I use braze-on centre-pull brakes on my touring bike, need I say more?

Cantilevers are to some the best possible brakes. For heavy use there is no doubt cantilevers are good. They are cheap, light and small; having little material means there is less to flex. Pivots have to be brazed to the frame but that is without detriment to the structure and is not excessively expensive. Pivot positioning is less critical today as most modern cantilever stirrups allow both vertical and angular variations. This can be used to advantage for those not sure about wheel size, 27in or 700c. Positioning the cantilever boss half-way between the two will allow both wheel sizes to be used – the blocks at the top of the slot with 27in and at the bottom with 700c.

Most models work well but you can, if you choose carefully, select a design that best complements your frame and wheel choice. Dia-Compe cantilevers have horizontal arms; Shimano and Suntour have their arms pointing to the sky, claiming the angle between the stirrup arm and straddle wire should be 90 degrees. That is, of course, incorrect but it does allow for variety, which can be used to your advantage. If your frame has a wide fork crown and you use narrow rims, buy horizontal-arm cantilevers. Conversely, if you have a narrow crown and wide rims, use a modern Shimano type where the arms are designed to be more upright. Both combinations will finish with their arms at a similar angle, somewhere between flat and up a bit.

Drum brakes are good today. Better designs have large ribs on the drum's outer wall which dissipates heat and stops distortion. If the drum goes oval even just slightly, brake efficiency will disappear. One design of drum brake to be wary of is the type where spokes are threaded through a flange that forms part of the drum's braking surface. Rim buckles, and any occasion when spokes have to be retensioned, can cause ovality. Without doubt, the best drum brakes are those that screw on to a block thread, for use with a double-sided hub at the rear or a rear hub used in an extra-wide front fork.

Drum brakes are often used as it is thought they are better protected from the weather – rim brakes being slow to stop in the rain. In most cases this is so, but should a drum brake get wet inside it will be totally ineffective and take a considerable time to dry out, if it does at all. Drum brakes at deep fords are potential killers and this is why my ATB has cantilevers. All I am trying to say is, do not forget the limitations of whichever braking system you choose. Understand potential problems and ride within your brake's capabilities.

Disc brakes are rare and expensive. Phil Wood, of the USA, market the most famous and infamous. It is novel in that a fibre disc rotates with the wheel and two stationary alloy rings crush the disc over its total area. It is an effective brake but disc failures have been common. The design has been upgraded and the problem apparently solved. Schwinn of the USA made a more conventional disc brake, looking more like a miniature motor bike version, but it is no longer available.

Brake levers are fairly simple devices. Some makes, such as CLB of France, are available in different sizes to suit giant, medium or small hands – something overlooked by most suppliers and something not realised by many cyclists, especially those with tiny hands. It is awful and dangerous not being able to reach the lever without removing your hand from the handlebar. A few modern, lever designs incorporate reach adjustment via a little screw. These must be praised as they, at least, make an attempt to alleviate the reach problem.

For tandem use, or for disabled persons who can only use one hand, brake levers are made to accept two cables. These can operate two brakes at the same time but they are tricky to set up for optimum effect. By nature of the two cables exiting the lever, adjusters cannot be incorporated into the lever. For fine-tuning of twin brakes it helps if adjusters are designed into both lines. Side-pulls usually have adjusters in the stirrup arms but centre-pulls need their adjusters on the head set and rear-seat-cluster outer-casing stops.

I use a twin-cable lever on my tandem to operate front and rear cantilevers together. I adjust the cables so the rear cantilever comes on fractionally sooner

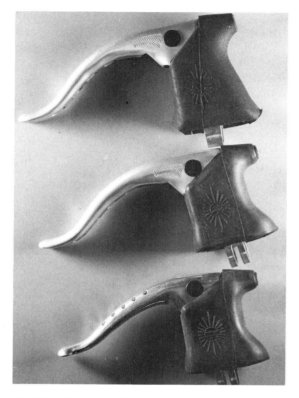

Fig 130　Three brake levers from CLB.
Large, medium and small depending on your hand size. Typical detail offered from France where cycling is No. 1.

than the front. The rear brake cable is three times longer than the front cable, thus it stretches more. By the time I have taken a big handful of brake lever, both cantilevers are working hard and I stop with amazing speed.

CLB are again worthy of a mention: their range of levers can be converted to take double cables at the cost of only a few pence – a good buy if you are experimenting. Aero levers is a peculiar name for a system where the brake cables exit the rear of the lever body, to go either inside or along the outside of the handlebar. The levers do not look different, except that they do not have the normal cables rising up into the air. They are aimed at the racing market but I believe they have merit for light touring, offering clutter-free access to the handlebar bag. Forget their aerodynamic properties, that is a load of nonsense. The disadvantage is that cable replacement is much more difficult.

I mentioned earlier the mechanical advantages of side-pulls and centre-pulls. The arguments presented assume that all the levers pull cables in an identical way. Some makes of aero levers offer non-standard cable movements due to the unique direction of cable pull and their pivot position. Some aero levers are there-fore more suited to side-pull brakes than to centre-pulls or cantilevers.

HANDLEBARS, STEMS, PEDALS AND SADDLES

Most of these items are chosen according to personal preference and there are no profound scientific topics to debate.

I know *randonneur* handlebars are supposed to be popular and recommended for touring, although personally I have little evidence to support this. I do not like them: they are narrow along the top which not only gives less choice of where to hold,

Fig 131   Uncluttered cyclist's eye view with Aero brake levers and hidden cables. Ideal for getting into your handlebar bag but a swine if your cable needs replacing.

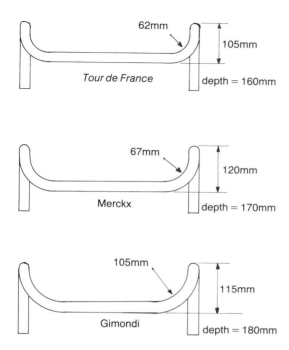

Fig 132   Common handlebar shapes – here,
the 3TTT range.

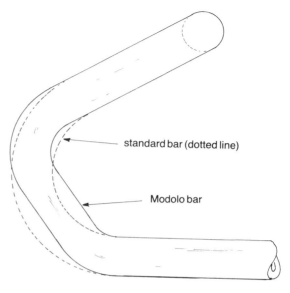

Fig 133   Modolo handlebars with flat,
ergonomic grip area.

but gets in the way of handlebar bags.
Most tourists I know use a wide square bar
as they do not like *randonneur* either.

Handlebars come in many widths,
several options of forward reach and
several options of drop depth. If you are a
small person, narrow, short and shallow
bars are the order – you may actually find
that a *randonneur* bar is suitable in this
case. Big, lanky cyclists are better with
wider, longer and deeper bars. This pre-
sumes that you are a drop-handlebar fan.
Many cyclists believe flat bars are better. I
do not dispute their reasons as most are
genuine but some cyclists claim drops are
no good because they never use the bottom of the bar. This can be due to several
factors: the bike is too long; the handlebars too low; or the handlebar drop too
deep. It all comes down to one problem –
the reach is too long. If your position is

correct it should be comfortable on all
parts of the handlebars and then all parts
will be used.

Standard drop handlebars are pretty
simple; designs between manufacturers
were basically similar. Then Modolo came
along and made the length of bar just
below where the brake lever fits flat, not
curved as is usually the case. This relieves
pressure on the extremities of your hand,
the points where a normal bar crosses.
The flat surface is extremely comfortable
and easy to grab; it is one of those simple
ergonomic design improvements you
would have thought would have been
done years ago.

Stems vary little within the quality market. Belleri, Cinelli and 3TTT are three
popular names. There are several standards for handlebar diameter and stem
hole size. Many cheap stems have a
25.4mm hole size and Cinelli and equivalent copies standardise at 26mm. 3TTT is
novel in that it lies somewhere between

Fig 134   The superb value SR platform pedal (but replace the balls with quality ones if you do high mileage).

the two, making their products incompatible with Cinelli. The only point to remember about the stem is to frequently remove it from the fork to clean and regrease.

Do not spend a fortune on pedals. Both the cheapest and the most expensive will break if you crash hard enough. Pedals on a touring bike get knocked around quite a bit. Buy a reasonable pair, such as SR's SP11 platform, a good compromise between price and quality. I have mentioned these pedals in particular as they are excellent and extremely comfortable, but their bearings are suspect. For a few pence I recommend you strip them when new, throw away the steel balls and replace them with some quality ball-bearings. They also come inadequately greased but once you have done both these little jobs they will go on for ever. SR sell a bracket that allows reflectors to be mounted to these platforms, a brilliant safety aid as most car drivers will confirm.

7 General Accessories

This chapter deals with all the bits and pieces, from luggage carriers and dynamos to side-cars.

LUGGAGE

When I started cycling I could not afford youth hostels (let alone bed and breakfasts). I had to camp with a leaky second-hand tent and a sleeping bag from one of those adverts in the Sunday papers. I became very fit and later realised that camping offers rewards not found in civilised accommodation – getting back to nature. I have been cycle-camping ever since and I still believe it offers unequalled freedom – there still being opportunities to camp wild even in Britain.

The trouble is the weight and bulk of all the necessities. Tent, sleeping bag, Karrimat, stove, pots and pans, fuel, water, the list goes on for ever. Although modern camping equipment has improved dramatically, it still has to be carried somewhere on the bike.

Pannier Frames and Bags

Respectable pannier frames are made by many companies and, for most purposes, alloy is finding favour. These are ideal for hostelling, club touring and the occasional camping tour; but I am not convinced about them for long expeditions. A guarantee card is not much help if your pannier breaks in the middle of Africa or Lapland. How do you get it fixed?

Fig 135   Cycle-camping offers untold freedoms.

Fig 136   *The price you pay is the bulk and weight but a price I still love to endure.*

On my 1986 ATB tour through Lapland I carried a short piece of brazing rod. If desperate I could have found some way to braze up my steel rack, something impossible with aluminium. Pete, my companion, broke his rack near the end of the trip and as it was steel we got it welded in a garage. Steel pannier frames are offered by several custom frame builders and are commonplace in the States. Bruce Gordon in Eugene makes a particularly fine range of Cr-Mo tubular steel, front and rear bicycle and ATB racks. An advantage of steel racks, even the relatively crude Kar-rimor steel-rod racks, is that they can be customised to take lamp brackets and water tanks for desert crossings. For heavy work, bracing struts can be brazed on and the whole carrier re-enamelled or plastic coated.

Pannier bags come in many sizes and are generally well made. Being old-fashioned, I favour cotton duck, as from the Carradice range, but most modern panniers are good. I have had excellent service from Karrimor Kalahari and I particularly like their mesh nets fitted on the outside that offer convenient storage for sunglasses and anti-mosquito gels. For rough-stuff and ATB riders I recommend small pannier bags and not low-rider front racks. If the bags hang too low it causes constant annoyance as bags catch on rocks, foliage and go under in river crossings.

Saddle bags are still popular in Britain. For some reason they do not seem too popular abroad but they have a lot going for them. If there is a choice I prefer a light pannier bag, the weight is lower and some saddle bags swing about if not well anchored. Handlebar bags are brilliant, somewhere to keep your valuables and easy to keep an eye on. But they must not be laden with cameras or heavy shopping. For documents, a map, sunglasses and a bar of chocolate they are ideal, but load them too much and steering oscillations can occur. Over-laden handlebar bags combined with modern steep frame angles are a constant source of problems.

Trailers and Side-cars

Trailers and side-cars can extend luggage space to ridiculous lengths. Do you really need to take so much that it cannot fit on the bike? Some people do and tandemists in particular run short of space – the same two racks as a bike but the luggge of two. Two-wheel trailers are dodgy, each wheel being vulnerable to road imperfections. Should one wheel hit a bump it can topple the trailer and you. I once had one jack-knife on a wet descent. They are not for serious touring.

Jack Taylor of Stockton-on-Tees makes an admirable single-wheeled device. It pivots on bends but follows the lean of the bike allowing fast and safe cornering. The single wheel is right at the back so the weight of the luggage is shared between this wheel and the towing attachment that bolts to the bike. Consequently, on a

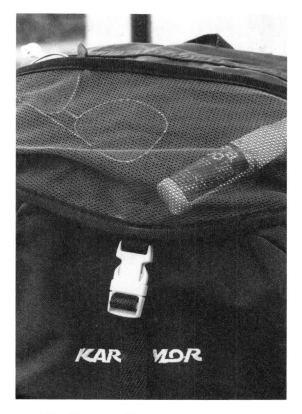

Fig 137   Net tops to Karrimor pannier bags are handy for your odds and ends.

Fig 138   The plastic bottle cage from Vitus.

solo, the overhang and forces on the tow-bar make the front of the bike very light. This trailer is better and superb on tandems or triplets.

Side-cars are better for light loads, such as infants. In fact they are safer for infants than a trailer, the side-car being inboard of the bike giving some protection. Most bicycle side-cars, unlike motor-cycle versions, allow the bike to lean in corners, not only making safer cornering but minimising the stresses found in rigid asymmetric three-wheeled devices. Modern side-cars are difficult to find although basic chassis are available. Most kiddy side-cars get handed down through cycling clubs or families but they can occasionally be found in the pages of *Cycle Touring*. Most pivoting side-cars allow quick detachment leaving just a small bracket attached to the left-hand chain stay. For

serious touring this bracket is best brazed in position as it is difficult to securely clamp anything to a round section, such as a chain stay.

Bottle Cages and Bottles

Bottle cages are available in steel, alloy and plastic. Steel ones are chrome plated which can be guaranteed to rust after a season, so the choice is between alloy and plastic. I have no strong recommendation except to advise the use of a complete loop-type cage when positioned under a tube. The weight of fluid in a full bottle can deform open cage designs and the bottle falls out. Most alloy cages are anodised and this helps to minimise the risk of alloy deposits getting on the bottle. Eventually, the anodising will wear away and black marks will appear. Plastic

Fig 139   Soubitez, bottom-bracket dynamo, seen here on a braze-on fitting which acts as the most positive earth possible.

cages, such as those from Vitus, do not do this, indicating that perhaps they are the way forward. They also fully encase the bottle making them ideal for under-tube locations.

LIGHTS

There are, of course, two reasons for lights in the dark. Firstly, so you can see the road; and secondly, so other road users can see you. Your choice of lighting system should reflect which of these two requirements takes priority. I live in the country, a very quiet part, and so I need to be able to see where I am going. That is why I use a dynamo. In the city, the most important thing is to be seen – to avoid being mown down. Many cyclists dismiss dynamos because they go out when you stop or because they cause too much drag. Both are true, but there are battery back-up devices and I can still go quicker with my dragging dynamo because I can actually see the road. Again, there is no ideal and personal choice is a good reason for whatever you decide.

Dynamos are either tyre-driven or in the hub. Hub dynamos theoretically offer the ideal housing but they revolve so slowly output is minimal and for that reason I dismiss them. Tyre-driven dynamos, both side-wall and bottom-bracket versions, revolve very fast and offer three watts of output, enough for some real light. The choice is between side-wall, often called bottle, dynamos, or the ones placed behind the bottom bracket driving, on the tyre's tread.

Bottom-bracket dynamos collect more road grime and must be cleaned more often. They are effective, especially the Soubitez model 80, but they make wheel removal a little more awkward, even with vertical drop-outs, and they cannot al-

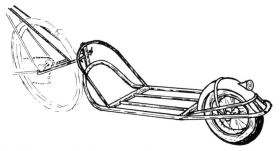

Fig 140   Jack Taylor single-wheel camping trailer.

ways accommodate a vast range of tyre sizes. You may wish to use the same frame with 21mm tyres one day and 35mm tyres the next. The profiles and diameters are too extreme to allow the dynamo to reach both without being moved.

Bottle dynamos should receive more favour. They are more tolerant to wheel removal and varying tyre sizes, but they are notorious for slipping in the wet. This can be minimised by putting a little rubber cap on the roller but it can be eliminated altogether by careful consideration of dynamo position. Normally they are positioned forward of a fork blade or in front of one of the seat stays. A spring pushes the dynamo on to the tyre but the reaction of the tyre, by virtue of its direction, acts against this spring. Mounting the dynamo behind the fork blade or rear of the seat stay means the passing tyre acts with the spring and drags the dynamo hard in towards the tyre. Give it a try – I think you may well be pleasantly surprised at how well they work behind the fork blade.

A word of caution: dynamos on the fork blade are best fixed to braze-on bosses. Clamps can come loose on fork blades, and as the blade section tapers from the top downwards, so a loose dynamo bracket will vibrate down the fork blade and then swing into the spokes.

Rear lamp position must by law be central or on the off side. Mounting rear lamps is always a problem. Custom carriers can incorporate brackets but fitting rear lamps to alloy carriers has for many years been a pain. ESGE have recently introduced an excellent little device, the J82S universal lamp bracket, just for this purpose. It is cheap and highly recommended.

There is no similar law on the position of front lamps so I mount mine on the left-hand fork blade just below the brake stirrup. A lamp on the right-hand side is more conventional but it casts a shadow of the tyre on to the verge and hedges. I use my lamp to see by, so being on the left the gutter is clearly visible. A car coming towards me cannot tell that my light is three inches away from the more normal position, so there is no detriment to safety. The lamp is not hidden in shadow until the very last moment but the car is going by at that stage.

I place the lamp on the fork and not high on the handlebar because the beam pattern is more spread. A beam pointing down from higher up only creates a bright local pool of light, either close to the wheel or far from the wheel, not both. The lower position lights both close and far and, being angled at a more horizontal angle, points straight towards car-drivers' eyes, appearing brighter. I do not necessarily recommend this set-up for city riding but it is ideal in dark country lanes.

Fig 141   Cibie bottle dynamo fitted to a braze-on boss on the leading side of a fork blade. Under the dynamo is a solid-state voltage regulator.

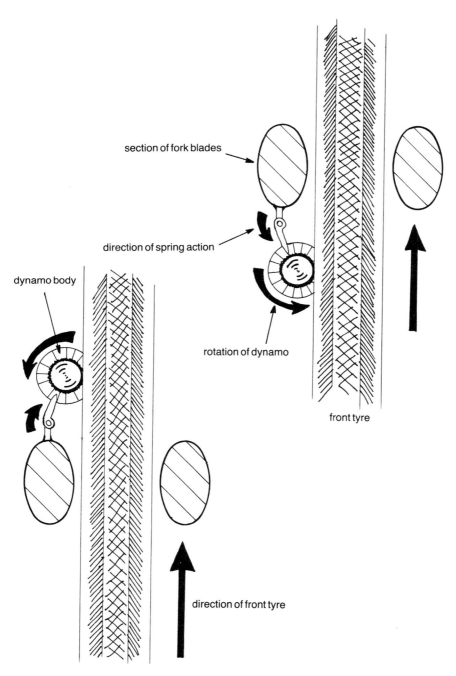

section of fork blades

direction of spring action

dynamo body

rotation of dynamo

front tyre

direction of front tyre

*Fig 142 Trailing and leading dynamo position on a fork blade. In the leading
position the dynamo is dragged into the tyre, by the tyre, assisting the
dynamo spring. Slippage is eliminated.*

Fig 143 *The lamp bracket that works, a little miracle from ESGE.*

Fig 144 *A Cibie rear lamp fitted to a Soubitez mudguard fitting bracket. A very difficult object to get your hands on.*

If you tour by night, in black places, do not forget a torch; road signs, maps and punctures are all hard to attend to with a dynamo. I carry a torch in the form of a front cycle lamp placed on the right hand front fork. Why carry it in a saddle bag when it can double as lighting.

If you choose a dynamo system, halogen bulbs can make for brighter and whiter light. However they are expensive and should not be touched by bare hands. Grease on your fingers will permeate the envelope causing darkening of the special glass. Use a tissue or if touched, clean as soon as possible with industrial methylated spirits or perhaps whisky.

To protect your expensive bulbs from power surges install one of the many voltage protection devices such as the Xi from Reflectalite. Power surge can come from bad joints or a blown rear bulb and the low cost of these small, solid state

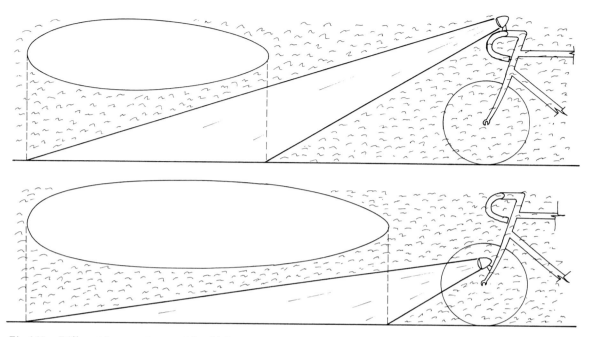

Fig 145   *Different beam patterns with a high and low mounted front lamp.*

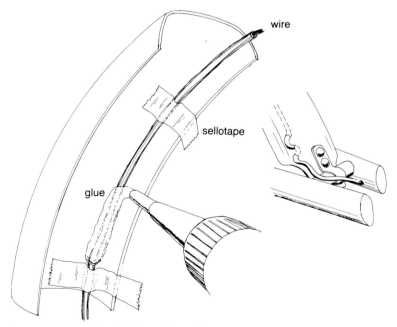

wire

sellotape

glue

Fig 146   *Gluing a dynamo light cable inside the mudguard is one way to make wire-runs neat and invisible.*

Fig 147   *Keep your wiring neat by winding it around a spoke.*

devices will soon be saved. It also pays to ensure good wiring in the first place and to keep the wire runs neat and hidden. Any floating wires will soon find reason to catch themselves and become broken.

I run the rear-light cables inside the mudguard. I roughly place the wire on the inside surface of a clean guard, sellotape it in position at about 1in intervals, and glue the wire between the sellotape with polystyrene model cement for chromoplastic guards. Allow the glue to dry, remove the sellotape, and glue where the sellotape has been removed. It is a slow process and should not be rushed but will give long lasting security. At the extremities, to minimise the pull on the wire-to-glue joint, I pierce two small holes and knot the wire securely to the guard.

At some point the wire must be free-floating in space. A neat method of forming a spiral-like design is to wrap the wire around a spoke. It then looks like a telephone cord and will help keep excess lengths away from mishap.

The most effective safety measure for night riding must be pedal reflectors and/or reflective bands on the back of your shoes. The up and down motion of pedalling stands out in car headlights long before any other warning system does. Pannier bags may partially obscure reflectors during pedalling but this, too, can still be quite effective by giving the impression of a flashing light.

I wish you safe and happy cycling.

Appendix I: Tube Sets

Key

UTS   Ultimate tensile strength, the higher the number, the stronger the metal.
DB   Double-butted, SB   Single-butted, TB   Triple-butted, PG   Plain gauge, DT   Double taper,
ST   Single taper, ID   Internal diameter, ROR   Round-oval-round
(all dimensions in mm unless stated otherwise. N/mm^2 is Newtons per square millimetre.)

Columbus MAX   typical UTS = $1280N/mm^2$

Tube	Dimensions	Gauge	
top tube	37.7 × 25	0.7/0.4 DB	orthogonal oval tube ends
down tube	41.3 × 27.7	0.8/0.5 DB	orthogonal oval tube ends
seat tube	37.7 × 25	0.8/0.5 SB	conical, oval end to round
head tube	32.9	1.5 PG	conical, oval end to round
fork blade	35.8 × 19	1.0/0.8	air profile
seat stay	21 × 12	0.5 ST	oval profile
chain stay	36 × 18.5	0.6	oval profile
steerer	25.4	1.6/2.5	with five helical ribs

Columbus TSX   typical UTS = $1030N/mm^2$

Tube	Dimensions	Gauge	
top tube	25.4	0.8/0.6 DB	with total length five spiral ribs
down tube	28.6	0.8/0.6 DB	with total length five spiral ribs
seat tube	28.6	0.9/0.6 SB	with five spiral ribs on lower butt
head tube	31.7	1.0 PG	
fork blade	28 × 19	0.9	
seat stay	14.0	0.7	
chain stay	22.2	0.8 ROR	
steerer	25.4	1.6/2.5	with five helical ribs

Columbus SLX   typical UTS = 1030N/mm^2

Tube	Dimensions	Gauge	
top tube	25.4	0.9/0.6 DB	with five helical ribs on butts
down tube	28.6	0.9/0.6 DB	with five helical ribs on butts
seat tube	28.6	0.9/0.6 SB	with five helical ribs on butt
head tube	31.7	1.0 PG	
fork blade	28 × 19	0.9	
seat stay	14.0	0.7	
chain stay	22.2	0.8 ROR	
steerer	25.4	1.6/2.5	with five helical ribs

Columbus SPX   typical UTS = 1030N/mm^2

Tube	Dimensions	Gauge	
top tube	25.4	1.0/0.7 DB	with five helical ribs on butts
down tube	28.6	1.0/0.7 DB	with five helical ribs on butts
seat tube	28.6	1.0/0.7 SB	with five helical ribs on butt
head tube	31.7	1.0 PG	
fork blade	28 × 19	1.05	
seat stay	14.0	1.0 ST	
chain stay	22.2	1.0 ROR	
steerer	25.4	1.6/2.5	with five helical ribs

Columbus SL   typical UTS = 1030N/mm^2

Tube	Dimensions	Gauge	
top tube	25.4	0.9/0.6 DB	
down tube	28.6	0.9/0.6 DB	
seat tube	28.6	0.9/0.6 SB	
head tube	31.7	1.0 PG	
fork blade	28 × 19	0.9	
seat stay	14.0	0.7 DT	
chain stay	22.2	0.8 ROR	
steerer	25.4	1.6/2.5	with five helical ribs

Columbus SP **typical UTS** $= 1030\text{N/mm}^2$

Tube	Dimensions	Gauge	
top tube	25.4	1.0/0.7 DB	
down tube	28.6	1.0/0.7 DB	
seat tube	28.6	1.0/0.7 SB	
head tube	31.7	1.0 PG	
fork blade	28 × 19	1.05	
seat stay	14.0	1.0 ST	
chain stay	22.2	1.0 ROR	
steerer	25.4	1.6/2.3	with five helical ribs

Columbus MS (Multi-shape) **typical UTS** $= 1030\text{N/mm}^2$

Tube	Dimensions	Gauge	
top tube	27.2 × 25.4	0.9/0.6 DB	double dihedral section
down tube	28.2 × 33.4	0.9/0.6 DB	dihedral section
seat tube	28.6 × 26.4	0.9/0.6 SB	conical taper
head tube	31.7	1.0 PG	
fork blade	28 × 19	0.9	
seat stay	16.0	0.7	
chain stay	27.5 × 18	0.9	RH, rectangular oval section
chain stay	27.5 × 18	0.9	LH, triangular section
steerer	25.4	1.6/2.5	with five helical ribs

Columbus Cromor **typical UTS** $= 870\text{N/mm}^2$

Tube	Dimensions	Gauge	
top tube	25.4	0.9/0.7 DB	
down tube	28.6	1.0/0.7 DB	
seat tube	28.6	0.9/0.6 SB	
head tube	31.7	1.0 PG	
fork blade	28 × 19	0.9	
seat stay	14.0	0.8 ST	
chain stay	22.2	0.9 ROR	
steerer	25.4	1.6/2.3	

155

Columbus OR MAX   typical UTS $= 1280N/mm^2$

Tube	Dimensions	Gauge	
top tube	37.7 × 25	0.8/0.5 DB	orthogonal oval tube ends
down tube	41.3 × 27.7	0.9/0.6 DB	orthogonal oval tube ends
seat tube	35.5 × 28	0.9/0.6 SB	conical, oval end to round
head tube	32.9	1.5 PG	
fork blade	30.5 × 25	1.2/0.9	
seat stay	16.0	0.8	
chain stay	36 × 18.5	0.8	
steerer	25.4	1.6/2.7	with five helical ribs

Columbus OR   typical UTS $= 1280N/mm^2$

Tube	Dimensions	Gauge	
top tube	28.6	0.9/0.6 DB	
down tube	31.7	1.1/0.7/0.9 TB	
seat tube	28.6	0.9/0.6 SB	
head tube	31.7	1.0 PG	
fork blade	25.4	1.3/1.1	Unicrown
seat stay	16.0	0.8 ST	
chain stay	22.2	0.9	
steerer	25.4	1.6/2.7	with five helical ribs

Columbus Cromor OR   typical UTS $= 870N/mm^2$

Tube	Dimensions	Gauge	
top tube	28.6	0.9/0.6 DB	
down tube	31.7	1.15/0.85 DB	
seat tube	28.6	1.0/0.7 SB	
head tube	31.7	1.0 PG	
fork blade	25.4	1.4/1.2	Unicrown
seat stay	16.0	1.0 ST	
chain stay	22.2	1.0	
steerer	25.4	1.6/2.7	with five helical ribs

Columbus Tandem CM   typical UTS = $1030N/mm^2$

Tube	Dimensions	Gauge	
top tubes	28.6	0.9/0.6 DB	with five helical ribs on butts
down tube	35.0	1.0 PG	
seat tubes	28.6	1.0/0.7 SB	with five helical ribs on butt
head tube	31.7	1.0 PG	
lateral tubes	14.0	0.8 PG	twin lateral design
fork blade	35 × 22	1.2	
seat stay	16.0	0.8 ST	
chain stay	35 × 22	1.2	oval as fork blades
steerer	25.4	1.6/2.7	with five helical ribs

Columbus Tandem CR   typical UTS = $870N/mm^2$

Tube	Dimensions	Gauge	
top tubes	25.4	0.9/0.7 DB	
down tube	28.6	1.1/1.0 DB	
seat tubes	28.6	0.9/0.6 SB	
head tube	31.7	1.2 PG	
lateral tubes	14.0	0.8 PG	twin lateral design
fork blades	32 × 22	1.2	
seat stay	14.0	0.8 ST	
chain stay	22.2	1.0 ROR	
steerer	25.4	1.6/2.3	

Reynolds 753   typical UTS = $1315N/mm^2$

Tube	Dimensions	Gauge
top tube	25.4	0.7/0.5 DB
down tube	28.6	0.8/0.5 DB
seat tube	28.6	0.7/0.5 SB
head tube	31.75	0.9 PG
fork blade	27.5 × 20	1.0/0.5
seat stay	14.0	0.6 DT
chain stay	22.2	0.6 ROR
steerer	25.4	22.31 ID

Reynolds 708 UTS varies.

Tube	Dimensions	Gauge	Typical UTS
top tube	25.4	0.9/0.6 Special	925N/mm^2
down tube	28.6	1.0/0.7 Special	925N/mm^2
seat tube	28.6	0.9/0.6 Special	925N/mm^2
head tube	31.75	0.9 PG	925N/mm^2
fork blade	27.5 × 20	1.0/0.5	802N/mm^2
seat stay	14.0	0.6 DT	1315N/mm^2
chain stay	22.2	0.6 ROR	1315N/mm^2
steerer	25.4	22.31 ID	

Three main tubes with special internal profiles, eight flat sides.

Reynolds 653 UTS varies.

Tube	Dimensions	Gauge	Typical UTS
top tube	25.4	0.7/0.5 DB	925N/mm^2
down tube	28.6	0.8/0.5 DB	925N/mm^2
seat tube	28.6	0.7/0.5 SB	925N/mm^2
head tube	31.75	0.9 PG	925N/mm^2
fork blade	27.5 × 20	1.0/0.5	802N/mm^2
seat stay	14.0	0.6 DT	1315N/mm^2
chain stay	22.2	0.6 ROR	1315N/mm^2
steerer	25.4	22.31 ID	

Reynolds 531 Competition   typical UTS = 802N/mm^2

Tube	Dimensions	Gauge
top tube	25.4	0.8/0.5 DB
down tube	28.6	0.9/0.6 DB
seat tube	28.6	0.8/0.5 SB
head tube	31.75	0.9 PG
fork blade	27.5 × 20	1.0/0.5
seat stay	16.0	0.5 DT
chain stay	22.2	0.8 ROR
steerer	25.4	1.6/2.3

Reynolds 531 Super Tourist   typical UTS = 802N/mm^2

Tube	Dimensions	Gauge
top tube	25.2	1.0/0.7 DB
down tube	28.6	1.0/0.7 DB
seat tube	28.6	1.0/0.7 SB
head tube	31.75	0.9 PG
fork blade	28.5 × 16.5	1.2/0.8
seat stay	16.0	0.9 ST
chain stay	22.2	0.9 ROR
steerer	25.4	1.6/2.3

Reynolds 525   typical UTS = 802N/mm^2

Tube	Dimensions	Gauge
top tube	25.4	0.9/0.6 DB
down tube	28.6	0.9/0.6 DB
seat tube	28.6	0.9/0.6 SB
head tube	31.75	0.9 PG
fork blade	27.5 × 20	1.0/0.5
seat stay	14.0	0.6 DT
chain stay	22.2	0.8 ROR
steerer	25.4	1.6/2.3

Reynolds 525 Triathlon   typical UTS = 802N/mm^2

Tube	Dimensions	Gauge
top tube	25.4	0.9/0.6 DB
down tube	28.6	0.9/0.6 DB
seat tube	28.6	0.9/0.6 SB
head tube	31.75	0.9 PG
fork blade	27.5 × 20	1.0/0.5
seat stay	16.0	0.5 DT
chain stay	22.2	0.9 ROR
steerer	25.4	1.6/2.3

Reynolds 753 All Terrain   typical UTS = $1315N/mm^2$

Tube	Dimensions	Gauge	
top tube	28.6	0.8/0.5 DB	
down tube	31.75	1.0/0.7 DB	
seat tube	28.6	0.8/0.5 SB	
head tube	31.75	0.9 PG	
fork blade	28.6	1.2	Unicrown in 531, 802 N/mm^2
seat stay	16.0	0.9 ST	
chain stay	22.2	0.9	
steerer	25.2	1.6/2.3	in 531, 802N/mm^2

Reynolds 653 All terrain   typical UTS = $925N/mm^2$

Tube	Dimensions	Gauge	
top tube	28.6	0.8/0.5 DB	
down tube	31.75	1.0/0.7 DB	
seat tube	28.6	0.8/0.5 SB	
head tube	31.75	0.9 PG	
fork blade	28.6	1.2	Unicrown in 531, 802N/mm^2
seat stay	16.0	0.9 ST	
chain stay	22.2	0.9	
steerer	25.4	1.6/2.3	in 531, 802N/mm^2

Reynolds 531 All terrain   typical UTS = $802N/mm^2$

Tube	Dimensions	Gauge	
top tube	28.6	0.9/0.6 DB	
down tube	31.75	1.0/0.7 DB	
seat tube	28.6	1.0/0.7 SB	
head tube	31.75	0.9 PG	
fork blade	28.6	1.2	Unicrown
seat stay	16.0	0.9 ST	
chain stay	22.2	1.2	
steerer	25.4	1.6/2.9	

Reynolds 501 All terrain   typical UTS = 802N/mm^2

Tube	Dimensions	Gauge	
top tube	28.6	1.0/0.7 DB	
down tube	31.75	1.0 PG	
seat tube	28.6	1.0/0.7 SB	
head tube	31.75	0.9 PG	
fork blade	25.4	1.2	Unicrown
seat stay	16.0	0.9 ST	
chain stay	22.2	1.2	
steerer	25.4	1.6/2.9	

Reynolds 531 Magnum AT   typical UTS = 802N/mm^2

Tube	Dimensions	Gauge	
top tubes	31.75	0.9/0.6 DB	
down tube	34.92	1.0/0.7/0.9 TB	
seat tube	31.75	1.0/0.7 SB	
head tube	37.00	1.5 PG	
fork blade	28.6	1.2	Unicrown
seat stay	19.05	0.9 DT	
chain stay	22.2	1.2	
steerer	28.6	1.6/2.3	oversize with 26 TPI thread

Reynolds 753 Tandem   typical UTS = 1315N/mm^2

Tube	Dimensions	Gauge
top tubes	25.4	0.8/0.5 DB
down tube	28.6	1.0/0.7 DB
seat tubes	28.6	1.0/0.7 SB
lateral tubes	28.6	1.0/0.7 DB
head tube	31.75	0.9 PG
base tube	38.1	1.2 PG
fork blade	31.7 × 18.0	1.4/0.9
seat stay	16.0	0.9 ST
chain stay	22.2	1.2 ROR
steerer	25.4	1.6/2.9

Reynolds 531 Tandem   typical UTS $= 802N/mm^2$

Tube	Dimensions	Gauge	
top tubes	25.4	0.8/0.5 DB	
down tube	28.6	1.0/0.7 DB	
seat tubes	28.6	1.0/0.7 SB	
lateral tubes	13.0	0.9	twin lats
head tube	31.75	0.9 PG	
base tube	38.1	1.2 PG	
fork blade	31.7×18.0	1.4/0.9	
seat stay	16.0	0.9 ST	
chain stay	22.2	1.2 ROR	
steerer	25.4	1.6/2.9	

Reynolds 531 loose tubes

Tube	Dimensions	Gauge	Length
top tube	25.4	0.8/0.5 DB	600
top tube	25.4	1.0/0.7 DB	600
top tube	25.4	1.0/0.7 DB	635
top tube	25.4	1.0/0.7 DB	760
top tube	25.4	1.0/0.7 DB	bent for low profile
top tube	28.6	0.9/0.6 DB	635
top tube	33.5×23.5	1.0/0.7 DB	635 oval speedstream
top tube	31.75	0.9/0.6 DB	635 Magnum AT
down tube	28.6	0.9/0.6 DB	635
down tube	28.6	1.0/0.7 DB	635
down tube	28.6	1.0/0.7 DB	760
down tube	31.75	0.9/0.6 DB	
down tube	31.75	1.0/0.7 DB	635
down tube	33.5×23.5	1.0/0.7 DB	635 oval speedstream
down tube	34.92	1.0/0.7/0.9 TB	635 Magnum AT
seat tube	28.6	0.8/0.5 SB	635
seat tube	28.6	1.0/0.7 SB	635
seat tube	28.6	1.0/0.7 SB	635 extra long 280mm butt
seat tube	28.6	1.0/0.7 SB	760
seat tube	28.6	1.0/0.7 SB	bent for low profile
seat tube	33.5×23.5	1.0/0.7 DB	635 oval to round speedstream
seat tube	34.92	1.0/0.7 SB	635 Magnum AT
head tube	31.75	0.9	220
head tube	31.75	0.9	300
head tube	31.75	0.9	635
head tube	37.0	1.5	200 Magnum AT
fork blade	27.5×20	1.0/0.5	370
fork blade	28.5×16.5	1.2/0.8	400
fork blade	22.0	1.4/0.9	370 for track use
fork blade	31.7×18	1.4/0.9	400 for tandem
fork blade	29.7×20.2	1.4/0.9	400 for tandem and ATB
fork blade	28.6	1.2	Unicrown ATB

Tube	Dimensions	Gauge	Length
seat stay	16.0	0.5 DT	575
seat stay	14.0	0.6 DT	575
seat stay	16.0	0.9 ST	600
seat stay	16.0	0.9 ST	635
seat stay	13.0	0.9 ST	1000 for twin lats
seat stay	16.0	0.5 DT	575 ovalled for speedstream
seat stay	19.0	0.9 DT	570 for tandem or ATB
seat stay	22.2	0.8 ST	300 wishbone for ATB
chain stay	22.2	0.8 ROR	410
chain stay	22.2	0.9 ROR	440
chain stay	22.2	1.2 ROR	440 for tandem
chain stay	22.2	1.2	460 single bend ATB
chain stay	22.2	1.2	460 double bend ATB
chain stay	22.2	0.9	460 single bend ATB
chain stay	22.2	0.9	440 oval for speedstream
steerer	25.4	1.6/2.3	240
steerer	25.4	1.6/2.3	300
steerer	25.4	1.6/2.3	380
steerer	25.4	1.6/2.9	240 tandem or ATB
steerer	25.4	1.6/2.9	280 tandem or ATB
steerer	28.6	1.6/2.3	215 26TPI for Magnum AT
base tube	38.1	1.2 PG	635 for tandem
base tube	50 × 25	0.9 PG	635 oval for tandem

Tange Prestige Super Lite   typical UTS = 1212N/mm^2

top tube	25.4	0.6/0.3 DB	
down tube	28.6	0.6/0.3 DB	
seat tube	28.6	0.7/0.4/0.6 TB	
head tube	31.8	1.0 PG	
fork blade	28.6 × 16.4	0.8 PG	
seat stay	14.0	0.6 ST	
chain stay	22.2	0.6	
steerer	25.4	1.6/2.0	with spiral ribs

Tange Prestige   typical UTS = 1212N/mm^2

Tube	Dimensions	Gauge	
top tube	25.4	0.7/0.4 DB	
down tube	28.6	0.7/0.4 DB	
seat tube	28.6	1.0/0.8/0.6 TB	at one end only
head tube	31.8	1.0 PG	
fork blade	28.6 × 16.4	0.9 PG	
seat stay	14.0	0.6 ST	
chain stay	22.2	0.6	
steerer	25.4	1.6/2.5	with spiral ribs

Tange No. 1 typical UTS = 894N/mm^2

Tube	Dimensions	Gauge	
top tube	25.4	0.8/0.5 DB	
down tube	28.6	0.8/0.5 DB	
seat tube	28.6	0.9/0.6 DB	double butted
head tube	31.8	1.0 PG	
fork blade	28.6 × 16.4	1.0 PG	
seat stay	14.0	0.8 ST	
chain stay	22.2	0.6	
steerer	25.4	1.6/2.5	with spiral ribs

Tange No. 2 typical UTS = 894N/mm^2

Tube	Dimensions	Gauge	
top tube	25.4	0.9/0.6 DB	
down tube	28.6	0.9/0.6 DB	
seat tube	28.6	0.9/0.6 DB	double butted
head tube	31.8	1.0 PG	
fork blade	28.6 × 16.4	1.0 PG	
seat stay	14.0	0.8 ST	
chain stay	22.2	0.8	
steerer	25.4	1.6/2.5	with spiral ribs

Tange No. 3 typical UTS = 894N/mm^2

Tube	Dimensions	Gauge	
top tube	25.4	1.0/0.7 DB	
down tube	28.6	1.0/0.7 DB	
seat tube	28.6	0.9/0.6 DB	double butted
head tube	31.8	1.0 PG	
fork blade	28.6 × 16.4	1.0 PG	
seat stay	14.0	0.8 ST	
chain stay	22.2	0.8	
steerer	25.4	1.6/2.5	with spiral ribs

Tange Infinity (Taper butted tubes)   typical UTS = 894 N/mm^2

Tube	Dimensions	Gauge	
top tube	25.4	0.9/0.6 DB	
down tube	28.6	0.9/0.6 DB	
seat tube	28.6	0.9/0.6 DB	
head tube	31.8	1.0 PG	
fork blade	28.6 × 16.4	1.0	
seat stay	14.0	0.8 ST	
chain stay	22.2	0.8	
steerer	25.4	1.6/2.5	with spiral ribs

Tange Prestige MTB Concept   typical UTS = 1212N/mm^2

Tube	Dimensions	Gauge	
top tube	34 × 20/30 × 27	0.9/0.6 DB	
down tube	34 × 30/30 × 27	0.9/0.6 DB	
seat tube	34 × 28.6/29.6	1.3/0.6/0.9	special bulge butt at top
head tube	33.0	1.5 PG	
fork blade	28.6	1.2/1.1	Unicrown
seat stay	15.0 × 19.1	0.8 ST	
chain stay	22.2	0.8	
steerer	25.4	1.6/2.7	with spiral ribs

Tange Prestige MTB   typical UTS = 1212N/mm^2

Tube	Dimensions	Gauge	
top tube	28.6	0.9/0.6 DB	
down tube	31.8	0.9/0.6 DB	
seat tube	28.6	1.0/0.8/0.6 TB	at one end only
head tube	33.0	1.5 PG	
fork blade	28.6	1.2/1.1	Unicrown
seat stay	15.9	0.8 ST	
chain stay	22.2	0.8	
steerer	25.4	1.6/2.5	with spiral ribs

Tange MTB   typical **UTS** $= 894\text{N}/\text{mm}^2$

Tube	Dimensions	Gauge	
top tube	28.6	1.2/0.9 DB	
down tube	31.8	1.2/0.9 DB	
seat tube	28.6	1.0/0.7 SB	
head tube	33.0	1.5 PG	
fork blade	25.4	1.4/1.2	Unicrown
seat stay	15.9	1.0 ST	
chain stay	22.2	1.0	
steerer	25.4	1.6/2.5	with spiral ribs

Tange Infinity MTB (Taper-butted tubes)   typical **UTS** $= 894\text{N}/\text{mm}^2$

Tube	Dimensions	Gauge	
top tube	28.6	1.0/0.7 DB	
down tube	31.8	1.0/0.7 DB	
seat tube	28.6	1.0/0.7 SB	
head tube	31.8	1.0 PG	
fork blade	25.4	1.2 PG	
seat stay	15.9	1.0 ST	
chain stay	22.2	1.0	
steerer	25.4	1.6/2.5	with spiral ribs

Vitus GTI   typical **UTS** $= 900\text{N}/\text{mm}^2$

Tube	Dimensions	Gauge	
top tube	25.4	0.6/0.7/0.9 TB	
down tube	28.6	0.6/0.7/0.9 TB	
seat tube	28.6	0.6/0.7/0.9 TB	at one end
head tube	31.7	1.0 PG	
fork blade	28 × 19	1.0	
seat stay	14.0	0.6 DT	
chain stay	22.2	0.8 ROR	
steerer	25.4	1.6/2.5/3.0	with helical ribs

Vitus TXO   **typical UTS** $= 900\text{N/mm}^2$

Tube	Dimensions	Gauge	
top tube	25.4	0.6/0.8 DB	special
down tube	28.6	0.6/0.8 DB	special
seat tube	28.6	0.6/0.8 SB	special
head tube	31.7	1.0 PG	
fork blade	28 × 19	1.0	
seat stay	14.0	0.6 DT	
chain stay	22.2	0.8 ROR	
steerer	25.4	1.6/2.5/3.0	with helical ribs

Three main tubes with special slotted butts

Vitus Olympic   **typical UTS** $= 900\text{N/mm}^2$

Tube	Dimensions	Gauge	
top tube	25.4	0.8 PG	curved for low profile
down tube	28.6	0.8 PG	
seat tube	28.6	0.8 PG	curved for low profile
head tube	31.7	1.0 PG	
fork blade	28 × 19	1.0	
seat stay	14.0	0.6 DT	
chain stay	22.2	0.8 ROR	
steerer	25.4	1.6/2.5/3.0	with helical ribs

Vitus Rocky ATB   **typical UTS** $= 900\text{N/mm}^2$

Tube	Dimensions	Gauge	
top tube	28.6	0.8/1.1 SB	
down tube	31.7	1.0 PG	
seat tube	28.6	0.8/1.1 SB	
head tube	33.0	1.5 PG	
fork blade	26.0	1.0	Unicrown
seat stay	16.0	1.0 ST	
chain stay	22.2	1.0	
steerer	25.4	1.6/2.3/3.0	with helical ribs

Appendix II: Summary of Steel Strengths

(All dimensions N/mm^2)

Type of steel	Tensile strength	Tube sets steel is found in
Reynolds 753	1315	753, 753 Tandem and 753AT
Columbus Nivacrom	1280	MAX, MAX OR and OR
Tange Prestige	1212	Prestige (road tubing) and Prestige MTB
Columbus Cr-Mo Cyclex	1030	TSX, SPX, SLX, SP, SL, MS and Tandem CM
Reynolds 708/653	925	708 Classic, 653 & 653AT
Vitus CR-Mo/Va	900	GTI, TXO, OLYMPIC, ROCKY (ATB) and KID (BMX)
Tange Cr-Mo	894	Nos 1–5, Infinity, MTB and Infinity MTB
Columbus Cromor	870	Cromor, Cromor OR and Tandem CR
Vitus Cr-Mo	850	XO, XO Track, 999NEW and 999ALPINE
Reynolds 531 Mn-Mo	802	531 Competition, Super Tourist, Designer Select, Tandem, All Terrain and Magnum AT
Reynolds Cr-Mo	802	525, 525 Triathlon, 501 and 501 All Terrain
Vitus C-Mn-Va	800	SM and STONE (ATB)
Columbus Aelle	720	Aelle and Aelle OR

Reynolds 653 & 708 Classic are sets of mixed strengths: the fork is 531 (802N/mm^2), the main tubes 653 (925N/mm^2) and the rear stays 753 (1315N/mm^2).

Appendix III: Listing of Tubes

(In descending order of weight)

Tube		Make/model	Gauge
top tube	1	Columbus SPX	1.0/0.7 with helical ribs on butts
	2	Columbus SP	1.0/0.7
	2	Reynolds 531ST	1.0/0.7
	4	Vitus GTI	0.9/0.7/0.6
	5	Columbus TSX	0.9/0.6 with continuous helical ribs
	6	Columbus SPX	0.9/0.6 with helical ribs on butts
	7	Columbus SL	0.9/0.6
	8	Vitus TSO	0.8/0.5 with slotted butts
	9	Reynolds 531C	0.8/0.55
	10	Reynolds 653	0.7/0.55
	10	Reynolds 753	0.7/0.55
down tube	1	Columbus SPX	1.0/0.7 with helical ribs on butts
	2	Columbus SP	1.0/0.7
	2	Reynolds 531ST	1.0/0.7
	4	Vitus GTI	0.9/0.7/0.6
	5	Columbus SLX	0.9/0.6 with helical ribs on butts
	6	Columbus SL	0.9/0.6
	6	Reynolds 531C	0.9/0.6
	8	Columbus TSX	0.8/0.6 with continuous helical ribs
	9	Vitus TXO	0.8/0.6 with slotted butts
	10	Reynolds 653	0.8/0.55
	10	Reynolds 753	0.8/0.55
seat tube	1	Columbus SPX	1.0/0.7 with helical rib on butt
	2	Columbus SP	1.0/0.7
	2	Reynolds 531ST	1.0/0.7
	4	Vitus GTI	9.0/0.7/0.6
	5	Columbus SLX	0.9/0.6 with helical rib on thick butt
	5	Columbus TSX	0.9/0.6 with helical rib on thick butt
	7	Columbus SL	0.9/0.6
	8	Vitus TXO	0.8/0.6 with slotted butt
	9	Reynolds 531C	0.8/0.55
	10	Reynolds 653	0.7/0.55
	10	Reynolds 753	0.7/0.55
head tube	1	all Columbus	1.0
	1	all Vitus	1.0
	3	all Reynolds	0.9

fork blade	1	Reynolds 531ST	1.2
	2	Columbus OR	1.1
	3	Columbus SP/SPX	1.05
	4	Vitus GTI/TXO	1.0
	4	Reynolds 531C etc	1.0
	6	Columbus SL/SLX/TSX	0.9
seat stay	1	Reynolds 19mm	0.9
	2	Reynolds 16mm	0.9
	3	Columbus 16mm	0.8
	4	Columbus SP/X 14mm	1.0
	5	Columbus SL/X 14mm	0.7
	6	Vitus GTI/TXO	0.6
	6	Reynolds 653/753	0.6
	8	Reynolds 531C	0.5
chain stay	1	Columbus SPX	1.0 with five ribs
	2	Columbus SP	1.0
	3	Reynolds 531ST	0.9
	4	Columbus SLX/TSX	0.8 with five ribs
	5	Reynolds 531C	0.8
	5	Vitus GTI/TXO	0.8
	5	Columbus SL	0.8
	8	Reynolds 653/753	0.6

Appendix IV: Favoured Mixes of Tubes

(In descending order of weight)

Basic tube set	Variations from standard	Duty of frame
Columbus SP/SPX	531 19mm seat stays, 531 chain stays if SPX too short	expedition
Reynolds 531ST	Columbus OR fork blades	heavy touring
Columbus SP	Columbus SL top tube, Columbus SL seat tube, 531 chain stays	general touring
Columbus SL	Columbus SP fork blades	general riding *randonnée*
Reynolds 531C	Vitus GTI top & seat tubes (or Columbus SL top & seat tubes)	general riding road racing *randonnée*

Appendix V: Tyre Diameters

Tyre size	ETRTO marking	External diameter (mm)
600 × 25A	25.541	595
600 × 28A	28.541	606
650 × 25A	25.590	645
650 × 28A	28.590	656
650 × 32A	32.590	663
650 × 28B	28.584	640
650 × 32B	32.584	661
650 × 42B	42.584	670
(½ Balloon)		
700 × 18c	18.622	666
700 × 20c	20.622	670
700 × 22c	22.622	673
700 × 25c	25.622	677
700 × 28c	28.622	680
700 × 32c	32.622	689
700 × 35c	35.622	699
700 × 1¾in	47.622	713
27in × 22mm	22.630	680
27in × 25mm	25.630	688
27in × 28mm	28.630	692
27 × 1¼in	32.630	697
24 × 1½–1¾in Road	44.507	592
26 × 1½–1¾in Road	44.559	653
26 × 1¾in ATB	47.559	655
26 × 1.9in ATB	51.559	669
26 × 2.125in ATB	54.559	670

Glossary

ATB   All-terrain bicycle (mountain bike or off-road bike). A modern concept developed for cycling use off-road.

Bottom bracket   The area of the bike around the axis of the chain set. In the context of frames it refers to the complex lug (a shell) which joins the down tube, seat tube and chain stays. In the context of chain sets it refers to the assembly of chain set axle, bearings and cups that allow the cranks to rotate.

Block   The freewheel assembly and cogs that screw on to the rear hub. Blocks commonly come in five-, six- or seven-speed varieties.

Butted tubes   A tube where the wall thickness varies down its length. Reynolds pioneered the process (*see* Appendix I).

Cantilevers   A very efficient brake, fitted to special braze-on pivots attached to the fork blades and seat stays.

Captain   The rider at the front of a tandem.

Chrome   A metal successfully used as an alloying material in the production of top-class steels.

Crew   The riders of a tandem or triplet.

Cyclo-cross   A racing sport for cross-country or specially prepared routes. Bikes are road-racing style with ample mud clearance for knobbly 700c HP or sprint tyres.

Dishing   The degree of asymmetry of the spoking arrangement on either side of a wheel. Six-speed rear wheels are heavily dished in order to accommodate a six-speed block. The block-side spokes are very tight and the opposite side very slack. A lot of dish causes weak wheels.

Drainpipe   The tube joining the two bottom brackets of a tandem. They are normally oval in section, 2in by 1in but round drainpipes are

still used (usually 1½in in diameter and usually for heavier frames).

Drop-outs   Fork-ends, either at the front or rear.

Gauge   An old British method of describing thickness of thin objects, such as the wall of bicycle tubes.

Fatigue   The wearing out of most bicycle components and frames.

Freehub   Started by Shimano and now available from Suntour, this is a hub and block built into one.

Head set   The assembly of bearings that allows the front fork to pivot in the head tube of the bike frame.

Honking   Riding out of the saddle, usually when going uphill.

Lost wax investment casting   Many better frame components are built by this process such as: fork crowns, bottom-bracket shells, lugs and bridges. It is a lengthy process that starts with a wax model, then a ceramic negative and then the final thing cast in a very high quality steel alloy. Each is a one-off, hence their expense.

Low profile   A time-trial bike built with minimum aerodynamic resistance, often with a smaller front wheel and upside-down handlebars; the front end looks lower than normal.

Lugs   Decorative bits that hide the machining and brazing at the interface of frame tubes. Some are fancy cut while others are plain.

Lugless   The method of joining tubes without lugs. It is equally strong but there are reservations. The joint is made with a fillet of brass filed smooth so the two tubes melt into each other.

Oversize tubes   Tubes of a larger diameter than normally accepted for that design. Commonly found on tandems and expedition bikes; they are used to increase stiffness.

Randonnée   A French-derived sport for fast touring, not racing. There are classes for all sorts and rides vary from 25–1000km (15½–621½m).

Silver soldering   Silver brazing with a brazing rod of high silver content. It is expensive but these rods melt at much lower temperatures than normal brass. It is essential for heat sensitive hi-tech steels such as Reynolds 753.
Solo   The normal bicycle for one person.
Stoker   The cyclist that sits at the rear of a tandem.

Tandem   A bicycle designed for two riders.
Tandem tricycle   A three-wheeled tandem.
Tricycle   A three wheeler, usually with one wheel at the front and two on a rear axle, although some trikes have two wheels at the front.
Triplet   A bicycle designed for three riders.
Twiddle   To pedal very fast in a low gear (making the muscles supple).
Twin lats   A pair of spaghetti tubes used in women's frames and for tandem internal bracings. They are not recommended as they have little resistance to most forces within a bike frame.

Young's modulus   The technical term to describe how material bends in terms of stress and strain.

Index